THE COMPLETE
COLONEL BLIMP

David Low and Colonel Blimp (Roger Livesey) during filming of Michael Powell and Emeric Pressburger's *The Life and Death of Colonel Blimp* (1942). (Photo by Bill Brandt courtesy of The Hulton-Deutsch Collection.)

THE COMPLETE
COLONEL BLIMP

Edited by Mark Bryant

Introduction by Colin Seymour-Ure

BELLEW PUBLISHING
London

OTHER TITLES IN THE CARTOON LIBRARY
(General Editor: Mark Bryant)

Gibbard's Double Decade Omnibus
edited and introduced by Les Gibbard
(Foreword by John Cole)

JON's Complete Two Types edited and introduced by JON
(Foreword by Lord Cudlipp)

The Last Bohemian: G. L. Stampa of Punch
edited and introduced by Flavia Stampa Gruss
(Foreword by David Thomas)

First published in Great Britain in 1991 by
Bellew Publishing Company Limited
7 Southampton Place, London WC1A 2DR

ISBN 0 947792 84 8

Printed and bound in Great Britain by Billings & Sons Ltd.

Colonel Blimp — An Epitaph

Here lies poor Blimp, the target of the town —
Still more alive than some who ran him down.
I never met the man. Nor do I know
Why all the clever lads disliked him so.
To be a Colonel, after all, is not
Conclusive evidence that one's a blot:
In fact, I find, in service or in shop,
It's not for nothing that men reach the top.

'Old-fashioned warrior' cry Smith and Jones,
Whose only form of fight is throwing stones.
Far back, he wanted England to be strong;
But even then the bright boys thought him wrong.
'Warmonger' was the name they gave him then,
And signing 'Peace Ballots' with a golden pen.
Let them confess, the lazy and the limp,
That no Peace Ballot bore the name of Blimp.
Indeed, the day the tiger springs my way
I'd just as soon that Blimp was there as they.

A.P. Herbert

PREFACE

T HIS book has been produced to mark the centenary of the birth of Sir David Low (1891−1963). Perhaps this century's greatest political cartoonist, Low was born in New Zealand and, after early success on the *Sydney Bulletin*, joined the London *Star* in 1919. He later moved to Lord Beaverbrook's *Evening Standard* where he remained for twenty years, joining the *Daily Herald* after the Second World War and then the *Manchester Guardian*. An immensely influential artist, Low produced over 14,000 drawings in a career spanning fifty years and his work was syndicated to more than 200 newspapers and magazines worldwide. He was knighted in 1962.

Colonel Blimp, who first appeared in the *Evening Standard* in 1934, was one of Low's most memorable creations, and his oddball sayings have been translated into twenty-four languages. Here, for the first time, over 200 classic Blimp cartoons have been reproduced — both from the original 'Topical Budget' pages and elsewhere — together with essays on the character by Low himself and others.

For their invaluable help in allowing access to the Low Estate's archives I would like to thank Dr Rachael and Michael Whear, Mrs Prue Rowe-Evans and John Appleton of Solo Syndication/The Low Estate. Special thanks are also due to Low's former editor, the Rt Hon. Michael Foot, for his excellent Foreword, and to the cartoonist's biographer, Professor Colin Seymour-Ure, for contributing such a fascinating Introduction and for much encouragement and support on the project. Many thanks too to the staff of the Centre for the Study of Cartoons and Caricature at the University of Kent at Canterbury — especially Liz Ottaway — for access to their archives and the supply of photographic material, and to Dr Angela Raspin at the London School of Economics. Last, but by no means least, I am greatly indebted to Ib Bellew for believing in this book, and in the Cartoon Library as a whole, and to Bob Vickers for its handsome design.

M.B.

CONTENTS

Preface   7
Foreword   *Rt Hon. Michael Foot MP*   11
Introduction   *Colin Seymour-Ure*   13

Vote for Blimp! — Blimp and the Government   31

1.   THE ORIGINS OF COLONEL BLIMP   41

'Does Colonel Blimp Exist?'   *David Low*   41
'Colonel Blimp's Ancestors'   *Robert Graves*   43

Gad, Sir, Peace — Appeasement by Blimp   49

2.   LOW AND BLIMP   85

'The World and Colonel Blimp'   *David Low*   85
'Blimp Marches On'   *David Low*   89

Splendid Isolation — Foreign Policy   93

3.   WAS BLIMP RIGHT?   109

'Marginal Comment'   *Harold Nicolson*   109
'The Assault upon Morale'   *Lord Elton*   112
'In Defence of Colonel Blimp'   *Arthur Bryant*   115
Letters to the Editor   *Lord Alfred Douglas*   115
'Was Colonel Blimp Right?'   *David Low*   117
'Was Low Right?'   *Colonel Blimp*   120

Fighting Talk — The Warrior Blimp   125

4.   THE IMMORTAL COLONEL   149

'Blimp Ascendant'   *The Times*   149
'Don't Let Colonel Blimp Ruin the Home Guard'   *George Orwell*   151
'Blimpophobia'   *C.S. Lewis*   152
'The Manhandling Democratic Touch'   *V.S. Pritchett*   155

Blimp on the Economy   159

5. *THE LIFE AND DEATH OF COLONEL BLIMP*   173

'The Colonel Blimp Film'   *David Low*   173
Churchill, Bracken and Blimp   176

A Blather of Blimps   180

FOREWORD

Rt Hon. Michael Foot MP

No great cartoonist ever set his mark upon an age more indelibly than David Low, and since the reader of this volume will quickly become captivated by the character of Colonel Blimp, first in the highly perceptive introduction and later in the cartoons themselves, it is necessary to be reminded that this was only one of his creations. One chapter of our rough island story might be designated the Age of Colonel Blimp, but it must be placed in its real context.

A full political picture of the 1920s, 30s, 40s and 50s cannot be composed without recalling the way David Low portrayed the politicians, and the way the politicians in turn conformed to his definitions, mockeries or indictments. The sheer range of his achievement is astonishing to record. He despatched Lloyd George's Coalition of the early 1920s to oblivion on a two-headed donkey, and lived to witness and deride the self-destruction of the British flagwagging imperialism which he so much detested in the waters of Suez nearly fifty years later.

However, it was supremely in the 1930s that he wielded his power, thanks to his art and his courage. All the miscreants among the leading Ministers of that decade retain their place in the nation's memory today in the style in which David Low painted them. This applies in particular to the two Prime Ministers involved, Stanley Baldwin and Neville Chamberlain, but hardly less to their principal accomplices and hangers-on, the Halifaxes and the Hoares. Indeed, the latest official life of Lord Halifax, the Foreign Secretary of our country at that most critical hour, shows that he was content, on his fateful visit to Nazi Germany in 1937, that protest against David Low's portrayal of Hitler, Goering, Goebbels and the rest should figure prominently on the agenda. When Halifax returned to London, the representations were conveyed promptly in person to the controlling authorities at the *Evening Standard.*

Colonel Blimp was given his place in that rogues' gallery, and since he could usually provoke laughter more than any sense of outrage, the question was sometimes posed, as the reader here may read, whether Low himself had not been unfair to the creature of his own devising by emphasizing his stupidities or follies in matters of such horrific consequence. However, it is worth remembering that the *Evening Standard* of those times was the house journal of the London West End, or what passed for the British aristocracy. In those quarters, David Low's radical commentary could provoke apoplexy. His Colonel Blimp offered consistent support to every policy enacted by Her Majesty's Ministers which were leading to the nation's ruin.

Occasionally it was asked, and not merely in connection with Colonel Blimp, whether David Low had enough passion or savagery in his own political character to enable him to match the finest achievements of his two avowed models in the cartoonist's art, Gillray and Daumier, or his great successor, Vicky.

No such criticism should be accepted: nowhere else, nowhere sooner and nowhere more consistently than in David Low's general 1930 output could our London, our England, see exposed the truth about the attack on our democracy and the pusillanimity of its defenders. It was not just a one-man show: there were some other political voices offering the same unheeded warning. But David Low delivered the message more bravely and brilliantly than anyone else. No one could stop him, and Beaverbrook, the owner of the *Standard,* was not fool enough to try.

One reason why David Low's political dedication was sometimes so mistakenly questioned was the diffidence of his manner. All those who had the honour of being his editor, as I had for a short spell, would, I am sure, offer this same testimony. He seemed to be perpetually inquisitive, always eager to discuss the latest developments in the political world, always ready to listen. Among his gifts as a cartoonist was his daring, original draughtsmanship, but this faculty was combined with a highly scrupulous resolve to study the great questions upon which he was preparing to pass judgement.

Considering how rare was his genius, his modesty might have been dismissed as a pose. It was nothing of the sort; it was part of the armour which enabled him to ward off his assailants. And at moments of crisis − and the most severe of these came in the 1930s − he faced enemies who would happily have seen him destroyed. The David Low of the 1930s was no licensed court jester. He was the leader of all that was decent in English public life, able to speak more boldly than others − thanks to that genius.

Once he had made up his own mind, he was not likely to be shifted, least of all by some intrusive Foreign Secretary whose quality he had already weighed in the balance and found wanting. He knew what the tradition of liberal democracy was, in the best sense of both those words. He saw better than anyone else of his generation how that great tradition was being betrayed and what was necessary for its re-establishment. All his energies were directed to that end, and his Colonel Blimp served that same cause. We can all laugh at his antics today but we should pause too to acknowledge how much, in that age of shame, we all owed to his intrepid creator.

INTRODUCTION

Colin Seymour-Ure

E VERYONE knows Colonel Blimp. Glance at these pages, if you do not, and you will soon find that you do. Blimp gave the order for the charge of the Light Brigade, as V.S. Pritchett pointed out in the essay reprinted here, and Blimp, it has also been argued, must have inspired Marie Antoinette to say, 'Let them eat cake!' Blimp it was, too, who wrote to the papers in 1934 to insist that the cavalry go on wearing spurs after they were mechanized, and who thereby prompted David Low to discover him. *Discover,* notice, not invent — as people soon remarked. The genius of Low invented the visual form, gave Blimp a name and a strenuous capacity for exertion, and reduced his muddleheadedness to neat absurdities. But Blimp's attitudes themselves were already public property: Low simply tapped a state of mind. 'I decided to invent a "character"', he wrote later, 'typifying the current disposition to mixed-up thinking, to having it both ways, to dogmatic doubleness, to paradox and plain self-contradiction' (*Low's Autobiography,* p.264).

Within eighteen months of Blimp's first appearance in the London *Evening Standard* on 21 April 1934, *The Times* noted that he had 'passed into the mythology of our country, to share the timeless existence of beings like Sherlock Holmes'. When Low broadcast his 'auto-obituary' in a radio series in 1936, the published version was headed 'Bereavement of Colonel Blimp', not 'Death of David Low'. He was included in an English dictionary the same year and was being translated into twenty-four languages by 1938. Many of his remarks remain fresh. Either they are of a general nature ('Exercise

PERSONAL OPINION
BY COLONEL BLIMP

Gad, sir, Lord Punk is right. Baldwin may have no brains, but he's a True Englishman.

13

the body from the neck down and the rest won't matter'), or else more specific but with a recognizable 'blimpish' attitude ('Baldwin may have no brains, but he's a true Englishman').

Low agreed that he had 'discovered' Blimp, and in 'Does Colonel Blimp Exist?' he wrote about how they first met in a Turkish bath. But he was exasperated by the extent to which Blimp quickly took on a life of his own. Low could control the name and the *visual* image, through copyright, but not the character. He declined, for example, to let people put him on the stage, except in a Herbert Farjeon revue in London which he endorsed retroactively. He also vetoed Blimp's inclusion in the repertoire of a celebrated concert-party entertainer and his use as a peg for a series of articles entitled 'Says Colonel Blimp'. The main exception to this rule was when he consented in 1942 to lend Blimp's name to a major feature film by Michael Powell and Emeric Pressburger. Low was always fascinated with cinema, and had himself experimented with animation in the late 1930s. (He would have loved the opportunities of the *Spitting Image* technology.) *The Life and Death of Colonel Blimp* was a major box-office success, partly because of Winston Churchill's attempts to ban it. Low enjoyed it — but noted ironically that his own image of Blimp as a muddleheaded ass was barely discernible in the sentimental screen version.

THE ESSENTIAL BLIMP

The essence of Blimp, as Low intended him, was stupidity. This was a — almost *the* — cardinal sin, in Low's opinion: 'To me there has always seemed to be more stupidity than wickedness in the world' ('The World and Colonel Blimp'). Even Hitler, he thought, was more stupid than wicked, and this attitude helps to explain the absence of malice from his work: Low's is always a friendly line. The sentimentality the film picks up is certainly there in Blimp, but as a very minor feature. Blimp is supposed to represent stupidity of every kind. 'Not of Colonels, nor of stupid Colonels in particular. Not of Authority, nor especially of stupid Authority. Not exclusively of the Right Wing nor the Left. Stupidity has no frontiers, domestic or foreign, party, professional or social.'

That is what Low thought. But of course he could not control the interpretations the world at large put on Blimp, nor the views attributed, by implication and often wrongly, to Low himself. He therefore quite often took up his pen, privately and publicly, to explain what Blimp was intended to mean and to defend himself.

This activity in itself probably did not vex Low. He was anyway an argumentative cartoonist. His cartoons are unusual for the number of words within the frame, quite apart from their captions. Low himself often appears, as a silent commentator, almost beckoning to the reader and seeking to engage him in the argument. His employer on the *Evening Standard* between 1927 and 1949, Lord Beaverbook, made a public virtue out of giving Low a contractual entitlement to express his own views — which differed largely

The first appearance of Colonel Blimp in the 'Topical Budget' feature in the *Evening Standard*, 21 April 1934.

REVOLUTION AT OUR TURKISH BATH.

BLIMPS RISE   GRAVE SITUATION

FROM OUR CORRESPONDENT: The Army has risen against Low's Spanish Cartoon.
Col. Blimp broadcasting, a proclamation from the Hot Room said :
"Fellow Colonels! These dam Spaniards refuse in the most dastardly
fashion to be saved by the Army from their beastly Government just because they
elected it. You can't have people telling the Army what to do. Gad. its disloyal.
To stop the Army from busting the whole show is destructive of law and order,
that's what it is. The whole thing's Bolshevism, of course.
Everybody knows the Bolshies want to destroy Democracy,
therefore you have them in Spain defending it...I mean
ter say...what's that?...Well anyhow, its Bolshevism.."

STOP PRESS
Major Moron and the 49th
Boneheads are attacking from
the North. Low has retired
to the plunge-pool and is
pretending to be a battleship.

Low's argumentative stance often led him into controversy, and floods of complaint followed his *Guardian* cartoon 'The Morning After' attacking the excesses of the Coronation in 1953. In an effort to combat the diehards he even briefly adopted the persona of right-wing cartoonist 'Mr High' (a self-portrait with a Blimp moustache) but to no avail. Low's attitudes during the Spanish Civil War also caused problems, as the above cartoon illustrates.

from Beaverbrook's and many of his readers — notably about the unwisdom (as Low saw it) of the policy of appeasing the Fascist dictators in the 1930s. There was thus a kind of implied disputatiousness in Low's very presence on the paper, reflected periodically in the letters' column.

But Low, like Conan Doyle with Holmes, did get tired of Blimp. Between 1934 and 16 March 1940, the Colonel appeared every Saturday in the bottom corner of a full-page cartoon in the *Evening Standard* entitled 'Low's Topical Budget'. This was a commentary on the week's events, beautifully designed as an integrated composition, and taking Low twice the effort of the normal half-page cartoons which he published four days a week. Some of the comments were political, some general; and a few other characters appeared regularly in it, including Low's dog Mussolini and the two dictators, Hit and Muss (later collapsed into one, Muzzler). The Topical Budget (a slightly odd name to the British ear, to which the phrase was unfamiliar) was an idea and title that Low had worked up in Australia, where he had made his reputation (after precocious beginnings in New Zealand), before coming to England in 1919.

Paper shortages killed the Budget after the outbreak of the Second World

MILITARY FUNERAL.

Frequent attempts were made to bury the image of Colonel Blimp, some of the more notable being those by War Minister, Sir Leslie Hore-Belisha. This cartoon appeared on 15 October 1937.

Low's farewell cartoon for the *Evening Standard*, published on 31 January 1950, with Blimps much in evidence.

War, but Low continued to use Blimp in his half-page cartoons. The larger space gave the character more scope. Sometimes Blimp might be the main focus, if the cartoon was making a blimpish point; at other times Blimp's presence simply labelled specific people as blimpish, through guilt by association. A single cartoon might be full of Blimps. Away from the Turkish bath, too, he might occasionally wear more than a towel: he appeared as Professor Blimp, as a Wimbledon ball boy, in tails, and in cavalry uniform.

Blimp's heyday (and, arguably, Low's) was the 1930s. But Low used him effectively in the war, latterly (and after attempts to bury him) as a foil when attacking opponents of postwar economic and social planning. He continued to find Blimp useful well into the 1950s, mainly to score foreign-policy points and to personify his critics. But by then he felt the character had generally outlived its value. Blimpishness itself, on the other hand, Low believed would never die. 'Without Blimp, history would be a barren record of progress' ('Does Colonel Blimp Exist?').

To Beaverbrook's deep regret Low left the *Evening Standard* in 1949 in a mood of restlessness. After an unsettled time on the Labour-controlled *Daily Herald,* which gave him an audience of two million — about three times the size of the *Evening Standard*'s (and very much less middle-class) — he moved comfortably to the (*Manchester*) *Guardian* in 1952, staying there, celebrated, knighted, and world-famous, until his death in 1963. This was the true 'bereavement of Colonel Blimp . . .'

WHO ARE THE BLIMPS?

Blimp's success came partly from his very ambiguity. He meant something to everyone — but not the *same* thing. People could read 'stupidity' how they wished. All might agree about it in principle but disagree on how you recognized it in practice. Low's critics complained, for example, that he attacked loyalty as stupid (as in 'The Government are going over the edge of an abyss and the nation must march solidly behind them'). But one person's loyalty is another person's obstinacy. 'Theirs not to reason why, theirs but to do and die.' That *may* have been a defensible attitude in the Light Brigade, but it is hardly a wise maxim for life. Again (and paraphrasing), 'It matters not who win or lose but how you play the game.' There are plenty of Blimpisms in support of that view too. Low would argue, however, that *unthinking* commitment (and failing to distinguish what really is, and is not,

a 'game') is the stupidity, not the principles of loyalty and sportsmanship in themselves.

The structure of a Blimp cartoon compounded these ambiguities, because there were likely to be at least three levels of meaning. First, there was what Blimp actually said: 'War is NOT inevitable, and it never will be unless we do something about it.' Next, there was what he probably meant to say, if you untangled the language ('. . . *but it always will be,* unless we do something about it'). Thirdly, there was the judgement Low intended us to make about either or both of those meanings.

What *did* Low think? The little man alongside Blimp in the cartoons — quizzical? perplexed? dumbstruck? — is much less certain of himself than the confident Low of photographs and real life. Low brought with him from the Antipodes a robust and practical political radicalism. Too much of an individualist to be a contented party man (which explained his discomfort on the *Daily Herald*), he inclined, nevertheless, to the Left.

Despite Low's protestations, therefore, Blimp was widely seen as an attack on the supposed stupidity of Conservatism and the officer class. The 'Colonel' prefix, which helped to set the character up, was undoubtedly a limitation. It made the depiction of left-wing stupidity so much more difficult that Low had to invent 'Pmilb', Blimp's long-lost left-wing brother, who stood on his head. Yet Pmilb's comments lack Blimp's bite, and the device was as clumsy as its name was awkward. 'Bishop Blimp' and 'Dr Blimp', which Low considered as alternatives to the Colonel, would have caused similar difficulties.

Blimp was thus successful in the characteristically journalistic sense that he was controversial, as distinct from uniformly popular. As public property,

STRANGER INVADES TURKISH BATH
PMILB CONFRONTS BLIMP

(The intruder, who claims to be Colonel Blimp's long-lost brother, insists on sharing the Colonel's limelight. This is going to be very embarrassing since he habitually maintains an inverted position, and his views while they are truly Blimpic, seem to have a Leftish tendency. More later.)

Gracious, ma'am, Lord Ditherwit is right. Pacifism even unto the annihilation of peace.

"I AM NOT ASSOCIATED WITH COLONEL BLIMPS" *SAYS INSKIP, 18/2/37.*

FORMATION OF A "BLUE DIVISION"

and as a verbal device, he was easily imitated. Friends and strangers wrote to Low, adopting Blimp's style and beginning 'Gad, sir!', either to applaud or to complain. More than once, he was invoked in the House of Commons: Ministers insistently dissociated themselves from any hint of blimpery, and War Minister Leslie Hore-Belisha announced in May 1939 that he had buried Blimp long ago. His military background, of course, made him much quoted in the war.

Observing the varied reactions, Low decided in 1942 ('Was Blimp Right?') that opinions fell roughly into three categories. Some people believed Blimp was intended as a destructive representation of something bad and was therefore to be approved. Others, however, (Low's critics) thought him a destructive misrepresentation of something good, and therefore to be disapproved (see the Nicolson and Bryant articles in this volume, for example). Others again thought him a misrepresentation that was intended to be destructive but backfired on the artist because the misrepresentation only proved its true goodness. Consistent with those divergent views, Harold Nicolson doubted whether he could find seven or eight people who really held Blimp's opinions; while the American journalist Ray Daniell, also in 1942 and in the same city, reported that 'It's impossible to live in London long without encountering the Old Colonel.'

In the same article Low reported an analysis of more than 260 appearances by Blimp up to that time. The fact that he bothered to do this calculation shows how seriously he took the arguments about Blimp's character. The bias towards diehard subjects is clear:

Military virtues (and vices)	7
Feudal-aristocratic tradition	3
Home and Empire policy	69
Foreign policy	139
Miscellaneous	47

CHARACTERIZING BLIMP

Controversy marks success of a kind. But the unique and unambiguous quality of Blimp, and for many of his followers the great joy, was the drawing. Nakedness and the anonymity of a Turkish bath detached Blimp from too specific an environment and made it easier for Low to claim that he was criticizing all and every stupidity. Nakedness suggests vulnerability, too,

---

Opposite: Blimps and blimpery often cropped up in Parliamentary debates in the 1930s and 40s and *Hansard* records Major Legge-Bourke MP attacking Low as a 'Communist' whilst seeing it as a 'great compliment' to be classed as a blimp. Defence Minister Sir Thomas Inskip (*above*) was evidently less keen, and Leader of the House Sir Stafford Cripps blamed blimpery and the 'Colonel Blimp mentality' for the loss of parts of the British Empire. When Capt. L.D. Gammans MP defended the Tory attitude to controls, Low decided to hit back (*below*).

REFLECTIONS ABOUT WAR, BY A SYDNEY ARTIST

An early forerunner of Blimp from the *Sydney Bulletin*, 27 August 1914.

and strips away the protection of rank. It also betrays Blimp's obesity — a physique often associated with complacency, petulance and sloth of mind. Steam, hot air and perspiration conspire with this to present a figure on the point of explosion (often suggested by a heavily shaded complexion), whom

Diehard Mentality

The diehard dimwits from the London *Star* of 8 April 1927 clearly anticipate the Colonel Blimp of seven years later.

Low then delights to burst with the pinprick of its own absurdities. The walrus moustache is a splendid tab of identity, adding an animal touch that reinforces the image of snort and bluster. Yet it is a sympathetic portrait: Blimp never looks threatening or nasty. The fact that someone is stupid, Low argued, is no reason to dislike him. Fat can be friendly too.

Low was no habitué of the Turkish bath, a place and pastime that had already faded from fashion by the 1930s. He 'found' Blimp in one which he happened to be visiting for an *Evening Standard* feature (in the series 'Low and Terry'), when he overheard a blimpish conversation between 'two pink, sweating chaps of military bearing'. These chaps were a stock physical type — portly, peppery, probably bald. Other cartoonists, such as Will Dyson, H.M. Bateman and J. Millar Watt (in his strip 'Pop') had evolved stereotype colonels. Precursors of Blimp also crop up in Low's own Australian cartoons; and his cartoon of 'Diehard Dimwits' in the London evening *Star* in 1927 anticipates blimpish sentiments, but in the mouths of slimline diehards (like Bateman's) who are blimpish only in their baldness and walrus moustaches. Low's Blimp is a distinctive varation of a recognizable general type.

Low hit on Blimp's name as well as the physique and location, *after* he had defined the character. Air balloons had been known as 'blimps' since the First World War, though the origin of the name is disputed; and of course 'blimp' was an affectionate name for the barrage balloons over British cities in the Second World War. Once Low thought of it, he cannot have hesitated for a moment. 'Colonel Blimp, of course!'

When Blimp was in a small corner of the Topical Budget, Low worked hard to vary the visual interest. The Turkish bath gave surprising scope (and prompted the marketing of Blimp-decorated bathroom tiles). An impassive masseur sometimes subjects Blimp to indignities, such as pouring a bucket of water over him or massaging his belly with a rolling pin. The equipment of hot and cold baths and showers provides variety; Blimp and Low indulge in horseplay with soap, scrubbing-brushes and broomsticks. When Blimp eventually breaks out, the remaining link to the baths is his towel. Low has him practise a truly astonishing range of sports — at least twenty-six. We see him doing all kinds of gymnastics; rowing, diving, sprinting, wrestling, bowling, putting the shot, throwing the discus, yachting, tobogganing, skating and cycling (with Low in tandem). He also plays hockey, baseball, rugby, water-polo, table-tennis, darts and football. Skittishly, he juggles plates, shoots ducks on a fairground range and rides the carousel; slides down the banisters, plays with a model airplane, and balances a ball on his nose like a sealion. He even turns up as a deep-sea diver.

Almost always, Low keeps Blimp frenetically busy, in conditions of physical stress bordering on extremity. (Even the temperatures of the Turkish bath are a kind of extremity.) He is constantly at war with the forces of obesity threatening to overwhelm him. These he tackles with the same explosive assurance and unreflective conviction that he brings to his politics. Blimp lives in a world of certainties. He knows exactly what ought to be done, in politics as in sport, and it is this strength of conviction which serves to point up his absurdity — just as people look more ridiculous when they do not know they look ridiculous.

This formidable set of physical recreations reinforces the effect of Blimp's verbal squibs. These take a common form, building in steps to a climax. First comes the exclamation: 'Gad, sir!' It is not clear why Low chose this phrase. Certainly it was archaic by the 1930s, and the *Oxford English Dictionary* cites no reference after 1875. But it announces Blimp's strength of feeling and works as a starting-pistol. Then comes the invocation, usually of a peer,

Some international Blimps — Low was keen to stress that the diehard mentality was not confined to Britain.

such as: 'Lord Coot is right!' Blimp rarely, if ever, invokes to contradict: he repeats and reconfirms an established view.

It looks as if Low had fun with these peers. Just occasionally he invokes a real person, such as Lord Beaverbrook or Winston Churchill. Often the titles juggle with bits of real name: Lord Fevermere (Rothermere), Castlebosh (Castlerosse), Snuffield (Nuffield), Tanglefoot (Tanglewood), Reverbeer (Leverhulme, Beaverbrook and Rothermere). But we also meet Lords Goof, Bunk, Tosh, Dolt, Mugg, Stiff, Flop, Punk and Phut; the Duke of Wigwam; and the polysyllabic Lords Sportingsquirt, Whistlespoon, Chucklehead, Ditherwit and Boopadoop. One might also mention Lord Bullswool, Lord Crackpot and Lord Mildew — and many more. If these examples, and Blimp's sports, seem quoted in excess, they are a reminder that being a cartoonist is hard work, as Low quite properly used to protest.

After this build-up the reader is ready for Blimp's pronouncement of the day. This varied in construction but was invariably foolish or self-contradictory — or so Low would have us believe. Sometimes it was an absurd proposition offered as a realistic basis for action: 'The country must face the alternative — wider roads or narrower pedestrians'; 'Hitler is right, children of five must join up at once to make the world safe for posterity'; 'We can't negotiate with that feller: he's on the other side'; 'Unless we withdraw our fleet from the Mediterranean, Mussolini will withdraw the Mediterranean from our Fleet.' These statements might also take the form of inverting a sensible idea to make it absurd: 'These measures against piracy are a menace to world peace'; 'The Spanish women and children must be taught not to drop bombs on battleships'; 'If the Abyssinians don't stop defending themselves, Mussolini will take it as an act of war'. In other moods, Blimp just spouted extravagant opinions Low disliked: 'To preserve British liberty, sir, we must lock up the entire Labour Party'; 'We must compel the unemployed to volunteer for the army'; 'Education must be stopped. If people couldn't read, they wouldn't know about the Depression and confidence would be restored'; 'There's only one way to stop these bullying aggressors — find out what they want us to do and then do it.'

Occasionally Blimp's self-contradictions conceal genuine dilemmas on which Low felt Blimp was taking a stupid position. 'The Tory party must save the Empire if it has to strangle it in the attempt': the logic of nuclear arms is precisely comparable. 'Hitler only needs arms so that he can declare peace on the rest of the world': this, again, can be read as a statement of the balance-of-power principle. 'We must preserve the sacred British right of free speech, but we can't let the wrong kind of people say what they like': here is the classic dilemma about silencing falsehood.

There is also a large category, easily the funniest, in which Low indulged his delight in word play. These are the mixed metaphors, the infelicitous images — gems of woolly thinking and garbled syntax — that produce an unintended meaning. With negatives removed, metaphors unmixed, or extra steps put into the argument, they quite often turn into harmless prejudices. 'Bayonets bring out the best in a man — and it stays out'; 'If we want to keep our place in the sun, we must darken the sky with our airplanes'; 'The only way to teach people self-respect is to treat 'em like the curs they are'; 'Eden is there to uphold British interests — not Humanity or Decency'; 'If things had been left to the High Command, the War would have been over in half the time for twice as many troops.'

FAREWELL TO BLIMP?

How much of Blimp now eludes us? Osbert Lancaster observed of the cartoonist's art that 'nothing . . . dates so quickly as the apt comment' (*Signs of the Times,* 1961). After more than half a century the nuances of personality and events that Low put in his cartoons have faded. The word

"It did the trick with Attlee... Why shouldn't it do again for this Wilson feller?"

THE TUMBRILS OUT AGAIN

The very last cartoon featuring Colonel Blimp published during Low's lifetime, this drawing appeared in the *Guardian* on 26 February 1963.

play and images, however, still appeal. Many of Low's general allegations of 'stupidity' still resonate, even if the specific references do not. 'Baldwin may have no brains, but he's a true Englishman' is funny because it epitomizes a certain enduring English anti-intellectualism. It does not depend on Baldwin for its effect. To later generations, it is a bonus if we happen to know the public reputation of Baldwin as a plain man's Prime Minister, but there is enjoyment enough in knowing that the remark could be made of any number of politicians in our own time.

Sometimes, as in the Baldwin example, Blimp's topsy-turvy statements need no gloss. 'What the country needs is less economics and more Royal Romances' is a sentiment for the 1990s, as much as for the mid-1930s. 'We English are quite right to be fonder of dogs than of Basque children. After all, dogs are our own flesh and blood' — that needs little qualification even now. 'These Americans will insist on behaving like a lot of foreigners' survives in the hankering for a British 'special relationship' with the United States.

In other cases we must remember that the siginficance of particular

Pastiche Blimps have appeared frequently in the press. During the Second World War the Soviet cartoonist, Boris Efimov, used the character to lampoon Allied hesitancy in forming a Second Front in Europe. The distinguished Australian artist Armstrong also drew some notable versions, and in the USA Cecil Jensen invented a parallel figure, Colonel M'Cosmic, to attack Colonel McCormick's journalism on the *Chicago Tribune*. More recently, in a salute to Low in *Punch* on 30 October 1985, Kenneth Mahood included a number of pastiche Blimp cartoons, one of which is reproduced here. (Courtesy of Kenneth Mahood/*Punch*.)

attitudes has changed. 'The Colonies must at once declare that under no circumstances will they hand over Britain to Germany' is a fair example. The absurdity of this view in the 1930s was absolute — Britain could no more be thrown out of the Empire than London could leave England. Forty years later, on the other hand, the possibility of expelling Britain from the Commonwealth at moments of isolation over her policies on Southern Africa was certainly mooted as a diplomatic tactic by a few Commonwealth countries.

Events and attitudes will always look different from different vantage points. Think what fun Blimp could have had with British membership of the European Community, the poll tax, the women's movement, the Green Party. Stupidity is in the eye of the beholder. Blimp will appeal as long as there are people who recognize his views as absurd. Let Low, appropriately, have the last word: 'Does Blimp exist? Blimp is immortal. As it is evident that there has always been Blimp, so it is too much to expect there will ever cease to be Blimp. Leave it at that.'

Colin Seymour-Ure is Professor of Government at the University of Kent at Canterbury and is Chairman of the Management Committee of the University's unique cartoon archive. He is co-author, with Jim Schoff, of *David Low* (Secker & Warburg, 1984).

VOTE FOR BLIMP!

Blimp and the Government

YOUR CANDIDATE

VOTE FOR BLIMP

AND

CLEAN POLITICS (H. and C.)

In response to many requests from the Hot Room Col. Blimp has consented to stand as candidate, upon a firm policy of shooting down politicians and establishing a Dictatorship of Colonels to safeguard Democracy.

MANIFESTO

Gad, sir, we must have a bigger Army to protect the Navy and a bigger Navy to protect the Army. Only then can we fight the French and the Italians and the Abyssinians and keep the war from spreading. There can be no Naval Agreement unless everybody is conceded superiority — especially Britain DAMMIT! We must have Conscription if Liberty is to survive — Gad, sir, I stand for lower Taxes on unemployed millionaires; and for raising the school age to cover Mr Thomas. I will abolish socialistic experiments like the Post Office and the Sewage System. As for the Socialists, shoot 'em all down and then make 'em work. BAH!

Gad, sir, Lord Beaverbrook is right. The best of our Democracy is that it gives every man a chance to become powerful enough to make a fool of it

BLIMP

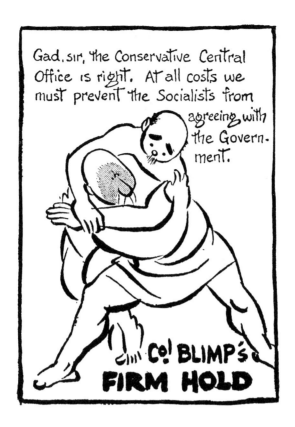

Gad, sir, the Conservative Central Office is right. At all costs we must prevent the Socialists from agreeing with the Government.

Col BLIMP's
FIRM HOLD

Gad, sir, Mr. X. is right. The reason our Government is always getting kicked in the pants is that it doesn't stand with its back to the wall.

ONWARD, COLONEL BLIMP

ESCAPE of STEAM by BLIMP.

Gad, sir, Lord Snuffield was right! If the country is to be saved from dictatorship, the House of Lords must put a stop to all this Democracy.

BLIMP'S PURGE

Gad, sir, Citrine is right. The Labour Party is quite right to expel all but sound Conservatives.

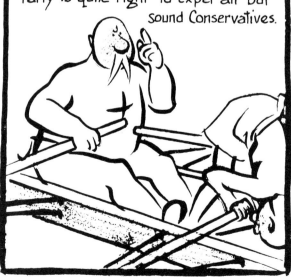

BLIMP THE BIRD-MAN SWOOPS

Gad, sir, Mrs Van Somebody Else is right. The members of the Govt. should all write their auto-biographies for £20,000 each and help pay for the new Defences with it.

BLIMP *IN THE COOL ROOM*

Gad, sir. Lord Gaspipe is right. To preserve British Liberty, sir, we must lock up the entire Labour Party.

Gad, sir, I ascribe my defeat to apathy and to the fact that 90% of the electorate voted for my opponent.

POST-MORTEM BY COL·BLIMP.

Blimp, who has taken up painting, is seeking inspiration in the Sahara. "It helps my political thinking" he says.

1. THE ORIGINS OF COLONEL BLIMP

150TH ANNIVERSARY OF BRITISH SETTLEMENT IN AUSTRALIA.

Precise details of how the British were first settled in Australia are in dispute, but Low gives this authentic view, showing Governor Blimp being bowled for a duck by Bradman's great-great-grandfather. Since then Australia has been settling the British pretty regularly, but why bring that up?

'DOES COLONEL BLIMP EXIST?'

David Low (*Lilliput*, 12 August 1937)

I T is always embarrassing to meet inconveniently curious persons. When a Nosey Parker asks me about Colonel Blimp I dodge the subject.

I have been caught — once, even, in my Bath. The superheated atmosphere of a Turkish Bath is no place for argument; so I have learned to avoid a certain retired Major who once, in a heated exchange of verbal perspiration, demanded to know why I was holding him up to ridicule as Colonel Blimp. It would be too exhausting to have to explain everything to him once a week.

Does Colonel Blimp exist? Of course. We met in the steam-room long ago.

I had entered thinking I was alone, but hearing an intermittent gurgling and whistling — 'Gagsrr . . . gagsrr . . .' — going on in the corner, I peered through the murky inferno and dimly discerned an ectoplasmic form, faintly pink, at the far end of the bench. It was Colonel Blimp.

In fairness I should not omit to state that the managers of that Turkish Bath maintain that they have in that steam-room a defective pipe which sometimes emits a gurgling-whistling noise, and also that there is at the end of the bench a boiler painted pink. No matter. That is where and how I met Colonel Blimp.

Since then I have met him regularly. But I have never seen him clothed; and I strongly suspect that he has no clothes. It may be that the trousers of his youth in wearing out assumed a symbolic significance, and that as a matter of principle he refuses to get new ones. So far as I know he lives at the Bath. To this comparative seclusion, presumably, may be ascribed the detachment of his views — detachment, that is, not only from unnecessary details but often from essential facts. I should find difficulty, on the evidence of our discussions merely, in giving him a party label. It would be true, I think, to say that by tradition he is what is called a Conservative — that is, he is non-conservative. In the non-conserving of British institutions in the past the fathers of Blimp were doubtless as proud to be useful as is the Blimp of today in the non-conserving of British Industry and the Capitalist System. As Blimps in Mary Tudor's time did their bit towards non-conserving Calais, so do Blimps of today do their bit in non-conserving Ireland, India and the rest of the Empire.

Blimp is Tradition. What was good enough for William the Conqueror is good enough for him. To the problems of the motor age he is apt to apply the technique of equitation; and he solves the problem of inconvenient plenty by using the economic principles of scarcity.

To the resulting chaos Blimp replies with the Higher Gymnastics. He Stands Firm, with Stiff Upperlip, Shoulder to Shoulder, Back to the Wall, in the Last Ditch, ready for All Pull Together, if he could only find out whom or what to pull.

Sometimes, when dozing off under my sheet in the cooling-room, I speculate on Blimp's family tree. The Colonel can trace his genealogy back only to A.D. 1066, but it is evident that to accept that as conclusive and exclusive is to do less than justice to his House. For history, to those with the spiritual eye to see, is clearly marked with the footprints of Blimp from the Dawn of Time. Truth is not always capable of proof in the narrow sense of the word, but the obstinate ass who would deny the plain evidence of relationship between Blimp and the Oracles of Delphi, for instance, would probably deny also the presence of Legatus Blimp in the Baths of Ancient Rome

('Jove, Caesar rectus est . . .') which would be absurd. As well doubt the attendance of Coeur de Blympe at the Crusades as doubt that of Blimp XVI at Versailles. Without Blimps history would be a barren record of progress, with no tales of how Blimp the Great burnt the cakes, or how Sir Walter Blimp played bowls before the Spanish Armada.

In doing justice to the root of Blimp's family tree, let us not fail to do the same to its branch; for I gather that, in truth, the family tree is not now so much a tree as a forest. Never have I met a man with more numerous and more powerful relatives. A family that in its present generation can boast of Mr Neville Blimp, the Prime Minister, Mr Herbert Blimp of the BBC, Mr Beverly Blimp, the noted writer on daffodils, Lord Blimp the celebrated economist, Baron Blimp the newspaper magnate and George Blimp the famous comedian, need have no fear for the survival of its importance.

Does Blimp exist? Blimp is immortal. As it is evident that there has always been Blimp, so it is too much to expect that there will ever cease to be Blimp. Leave it at that.

'COLONEL BLIMP'S ANCESTORS'

Robert Graves (*Occupation Writer*, 1951)

F OR centuries there has been an unbroken succession of Colonel Blimps. Recently in *The Times* two announcements, covering three generations, appeared on the same page:

BLIMP — At his residence, Limphalt Manor, Wessex, after a brief illness, Colonel Hereward Marmaduke Blimp, DSO, MVO, JP, late Umpty-Third Regiment, Royal Patagonians, aged 85. Funeral on Friday, 13th. Flowers by request. Indian papers please copy.

BLIMP — To Daphne, née Crimp, wife of Lieut.-Colonel Marmaduke Hereward Blimp, Royal Patagonians — a son. Indian papers please copy.

The ox-headed Saxon strain has always been dominant in the Blimp family. Qualities of shrewdness, wit, humanity, logic, resourcefulness, that intermarriage with more gifted neighbour races has grafted on our brutish Germanic stock, have never been noted in a Blimp. Historians and geneticians are puzzled to know how the family has survived so long and prosperously. I will try to explain this by a short family record.

In the reign of Ethelred the Unready there lived an old, bald, long-moustached West Saxon nicknamed Hereweard Belemphaltet (Hereward with the limp). Since the whole family was subject to gout, the nickname became hereditary and was shortened to Blimp. Hereweard, though an orthodox Christian, admired the pagan Danes as a 'fine soldierly horde of men' and approved of their raids on 'the base-born churls and mercenary monks of Essex'. He said of Dane-geld: 'Gad, sir, King Ethelred is right. The more we give the Danes, the less there'll be for them to pillage.' (Translation.)

Hereweard Blimphalt, the thane of 1066, refused to believe in the Norman danger until it was too late to take his company of spearmen to King Harold's help. William the Conqueror, judging him a loyal pro-Norman, let him keep his estate, which was three-parts marsh, on condition that he paid a token to the Crown of three marsh-mallows every Lady Day. These flowers appear in the Blimp coat of arms. The Blimps are proud of their picturesque old fee, though it reflects no credit on them. The Blimp crest is a mailed hand with a spear at the charge; this emblemizes the Blimp love of shock tactics. The Blimps always charge bald-headed at the five-barred gate, or the enemy's embattled centre: they scorn the indirect approach or the tactics of infiltration, which they think ungentlemanly.

At Crécy (or that is the family tradition) when the flower of French chivalry was first rudely greeted by the boom of wooden cannon, then galled by volleys of cloth-yard arrows, and finally carved up by wild Welsh irregulars with knives, the de Blympe of the day was scandalized. 'By Saint Ethelburga, my liege lord,' he gasped to the fighting Bishop of Wells, whose vassal he was, 'it grieves me right heartily that so gallant an array of Knights should be distressed and bloodily butchered by our base and vulgar commonalty.' (The Blimps have always detested irregulars.) He rescued a couple of Burgundian knights from the slaughter and did very well out of the ransom, which was paid in wine. This was the Blimp who said: 'I swear by God's Body, I would rather my son should hang than study letters!' He himself could not sign his name.

The Elizabethan de Blympe was satirized by Shakespeare as Sir John Falstaff. Shakespeare was rather too kind to him; but of course unadulterated Blimp is not good theatre.

The Jacobean Sir Marmaduke was the first Colonel Blimp. He learned his soldiering in Holland. A letter of his survives, dated 13 December 1641, from the Hague:

Honoured ffather:
Trewely, let mee travell whair I will, soe I go not to Hell, a more baser countrie than thiss for a jentill man to live I cannot find. I have bin much crost in my advancement by the jelosies of divers other offecers of this Regt. I besitch you send mee a nagg for I am so lame of the gowt I cannot march. And pitty your dewetiful sonn,
Marmaduke Blimp.

(The Blimps have always ascribed their failure to rise in the service to the jealous machinations of their brother officers.) The Civil War broke out in 1643, and Sir Marmaduke was given a company in a Royalist infantry regiment. He fought in several indecisive battles and refused to take the New Model Army seriously, 'beeing but a parsel of rogues, runagates, madd men and jack-puddens'. He regarded the pike, already obsolete, as the 'queene of the battle'. He held a strong castle near 'Sentellens' (St Helen's) in 1645 for some weeks, but then unwisely agreed to a parley with a Roundhead Colonel at a postern window. This 'currish dogg' plucked him out through the window by the ears; the castle surrendered. (The Blimps always fall for simple strategems of this sort.) He gave his parole not to fight again and laid low until the Restoration. Most of his money had been lost in the Wars, but in 1671 a Dutch engineer fortunately drained the marshes for the landowners of the district and added several hundred acres of good land to the Blimp estate. Fortunate Blimps!

His son became Colonel of the Umpty-Third Regiment shortly after its foundation in 1690 by King William III. He had his head removed by a cannon-ball at the Boyne, just after making this speech to his officers: 'Gentlemen, see that you show no quarter to these fubsy Irish papishers, seeing they are scarce to be reckoned human. Why, a sober man, well known to me, avouches that lately on the Dublin road seeing their naked corpses corded together in a cart, three of every five had long bushy tails like to a fox's.' The Blimps still believe all that they hear to the discredit of those whom Kipling has now taught them to style 'the lesser breeds without the Law'.

His son commanded the Umpty-Third under Marlborough. Marlborough gave them their nickname (now confirmed by Royal Warrant) of The Royal Patagonians. Someone remarked in his hearing 'the inhabitants of Patagonia are so rude that they cannot reckon numbers beyond three'. Marlborough replied: 'Ods Cock, that is one better than Colonel Blimp and his kind!' (It is true that the Blimps have never been strong at arithmetic and have always relied on a Scotch bailiff for keeping their accounts). Marlborough did not ask more from Colonel Blimp than he could perform; the Blimps have always been fairly good at close-order parade-ground drill which suited Continental warfare at that time. Marlborough with a few intelligent *aides* could manage the tactical and strategic side of the fighting. It was about this time that the Methuen Treaty with Portugal made port the family drink of the Blimps; and that the aestuary, a primitive Turkish bath, was invented. Colonel Blimp bought one; it is still in the family.

The next Blimp fought at Minden in 1759: mistaking their orders, the Royal Patagonians and five other well-disciplined British regiments marched out unsupported against three times their number of French cavalry and tumbled them to ruin. Colonel Blimp afterwards said to General Phillips of the Artillery: 'Ecod, sir, 'twas not such an encounter as I could have wished, being fought in no proper order. Upon my soul, General Contades did right to withdraw his cuirassiers when we came upon him so unceremoniously. It is not the part of infantry to assault cavalry, but clean contrariwise.'

The next Blimp married the ugly widow of a ship's chandler who had made a fortune by cheating the Navy. (This windfall lasted the Blimps until, in 1840, the railway came through their estate and kept them going another hundred years.) The Blimps always marry beneath them and never marry beauties; in consequence they are neither a handsome nor a well-mannered family. Under this Blimp the Royal Patagonians were led in 1776 against the American revolutionaries. They were cut to pieces at Bunker's Hill, reformed, and in 1782 forced to capitulate at Yorktown. *'Mong Dew, Moosoo!'* cried Colonel Blimp, as he handed his sword to General Choisy, a French ally of the Americans: 'I vow it is a pleasure to engage in civilized warfare again after these raggle-taggle catch-as-catch-can bouts with a mob of canting Mohairs and cowardly Buckskins who skulk behind trees and never come to push of bayonet.'

'Parfaitement, mon Colonel,' replied Choisy, not understanding a word of what he said. (As has already been noted, the Blimps are no linguists.)

Space presses: no room for a detailed account of the Peninsular War Blimp whom Wellington tried to cashier for incompetence, but who cleared himself at the court-martial by pleading that he always rode straight to hounds. Nor of the Indian Mutiny Blimp, who was deeply religious and rejoiced that he had 'implemented Jehovah's vengeance on those devilish copper-coloured Pandies by blowing a full company of them from our guns', and who afterwards wrote to the *Englishman* under the signature 'Britannicus': 'The only people who have any right to India are the British; the so-called Indians have no right whatever.' Nor of his successor, the famous Bath Club Bore of the eighties, who adulated the Prussian army, and who was enraged when by Act of Parliament commissions were no longer bought, but awarded by merit. ('Merit be damned! Gad, sir, what will become of us old military families?') He is the Blimp of whom Basil Blackwood wrote succinctly in the First World War *Hun-Hunters:*

> In times gone by, or so I've heard,
> He led the gallant Umpty-Third
> To somewhere in Afghanistan
> Where they were slaughtered to a man.

At the Bath Club he was perpetually:

> ... ventilating more of his
> Grievances against the War Office.

A word about the old man who has just died. He scraped through Sandhurst, where he learned drill and how to draw coloured maps, but nothing about geography or military history or field-engineering. In the South African War he despised the Boers as much as his ancestor had despised the American revolutionaries, and won a DSO (then a ration issue to COs and known as the 'Damn Silly Order'). A Boer Commando surprised the Patagonian headquarters one dark night in what Colonel Blimp had thought a safe area, and he ended the war in captivity. In 1914 he returned as a dug-out to command a Kitchener battalion: in 1915, on his first night in the trenches near La Bassée, he went out with a flash-light to inspect the barbed wire and, fortunately for his men, was put out of action for the rest of the war by a German sentry. He was David Low's Colonel Blimp, whom we all know so well. His son — but his son is still alive and, I regret to say, still on the active list.

GAD, SIR, PEACE

Appeasement by Blimp

GOOD RESOLUTION FOR '39

Gad, sir, we may lose Democracy, Decency, Liberty and the Empire, but we will defend Chamberlain's umbrella to the last.

BIG APPLE *BY* **COL. BLIMP**

Gad, sir, Garvin is right. There's only one way to stop these bullying aggressors — find out what they want us to do and then do it.

Col BLIMP PERSPIRES WISDOM,

Gad, sir, Mr. Lansbury is right. The League of Nations should insist on peace — except, of course, in the event of war.

Gad, sir, Churchill is right. Mr Baldwin has evidently made an irrevocable decision to be guided by circumstances with a firm hand.

BLIMP CRISIS

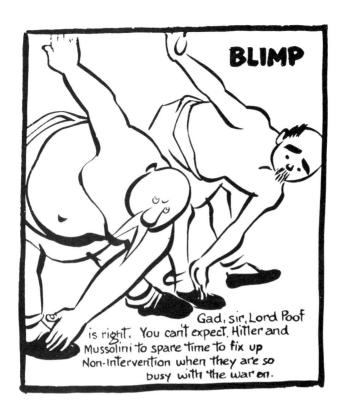

Telegram from Paris

All well stop spirit of unity being forged in waters of common goal stop great enthusiasm for M. Shamberlain whom called here Sham for short stop please send more expenses Blimp

Gad sir Vive la France

Gad, sir, Lord Busslepush is right. We must warn Eden that he is there to uphold British Interests — not Humanity or Decency.

SHOOT!   by BLIMP

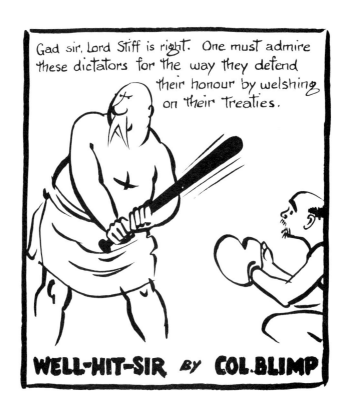

MUGS' MOTTO

STUDY IN STATESMANSHIP

MOUSTACHE DISARMAMENT

A meeting was called to discuss last week's order to a Coldstream Guardsman to shave his moustache. Col. Blimp was for battleships, and Lord Peel insisted on a 2-power standard. Lord Dawson and Neville Chamberlain favoured destroyers, but Harry Tate and Charles Laughton refused to cut down their airplane carriers.

Gad, sir, Lord Rathermere is right. We must have a bigger Army to protect the Navy and a bigger Navy to protect the Army. Only then can we fight the French and the Italians and the Abyssinians and keep the war from spreading

BLIMP

EXPOSURE BY BLIMP

Gad, sir, Lord Beaverbrook is right. This League of Nations is a big sham. Why, it's nearly all foreigners.

BLIMP.

Gad, sir, Lord Beaverbrook is right. The only way to ensure peace is to give everybody plenty of arms and let them fight it out.

URGENT PREPARATIONS FOR THE WORLD FLOOD.

ABYSSINIA

Gad, sir, Mussolini is right. It's an affront to International Honour to invite Haile Selassie to our coronation after the dirty way he tried to annex Italy.

BLIMP

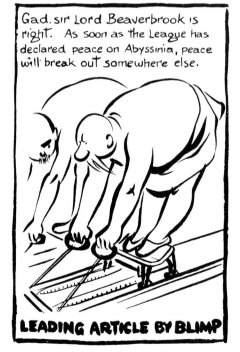

Gad. sir Lord Beaverbrook is right. As soon as the League has declared peace on Abyssinia, peace will break out somewhere else.

LEADING ARTICLE BY BLIMP

FREE KICK BY **BLIMP**

Gad, sir, the Government is right. We have to keep our word and let down Haile Selassie. Dash it, its the only decent thing to do.

Gad, sir, Lord Beaverbrook is right. If the Abyssinians dont stop defending themselves, Mussolini will take it as an act of war.

COL. BLIMP'S WARNING.

HANDSPRING
BY
Col. BLIMP

Gad, sir,
Mussolini is
right. There can
be no negotiations
until Geneva is
moved to somewhere else.

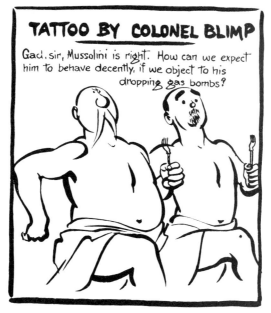

TATTOO BY COLONEL BLIMP

Gad, sir, Mussolini is right. How can we expect
him to behave decently, if we object to his
dropping gas bombs?

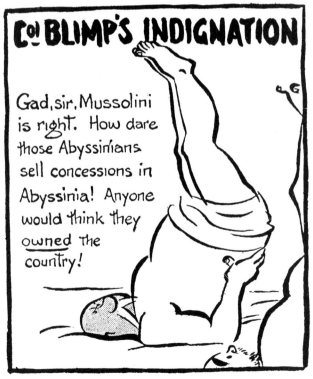

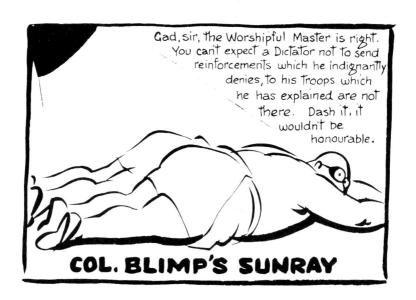

COL. BLIMP'S SUNRAY

HOT RETURN
BY
COL. BLIMP

SPURT BY Col. BLIMP

Gad, sir, Lord Wallop is right. How can the black savages learn how to use poison gas unless they surrender to Italian civilization?

Gad, sir, Haile Selassie is right. Our Flood-Prevention Authorities will now cease their campaign until after the rains.

Col. BLIMP SPRINTS

SPAIN

COL. BLIMP AND THE B.B.C.

To meet certain criticisms of the alleged "redness" of News Bulletins, the B.B.C. is about to appoint a new announcer whose well-known fairness of tone and view should satisfy the most rampantly "impartial" anti-red.

"Gad, listeners, Reuter, the Central News and Exchange are right! The Madrid Government are being beaten, the dirty skunks, and their atheistic army is in flight. Theee impartial cheers for Franco!"

Gad, sir, Franco is right. The women and children of Guernica just massacred themselves for spite.

Col. BLIMP's DECORATIONS

MANCHURIA

Gad, sir, Lord Poppycock is right.
We can't declare a boycott of Japanese
goods, because then how could Japan
pay innocent business men for the raw
materials to make their bombs.?

FITNESS *BY* **COL. BLIMP**

Gad, sir, Lord Foozle is right.
The Japanese are only
killing the Chinese to
save them from
their enemies.

HOLE *By* **COL BLIMP**

71

PLAY THE GAME! by BLIMP

GERMANY

PEACEMAKER BLIMP

'Gad, sir, Lord Hysteria is right. If Hitler starts making trouble about colonies, Britain should follow a policy of strict Non-intervention. KEEP-OUT-AND-STAY-OUT!—what?'

'Gad, sir, Hitler is right. The nations could all pull together if only we allowed him to settle whom to pull.

BLIMP ON THE LINE

BLIMP'S EAR *TO THE* GROUND

FROM COL. BLIMP'S ANGLE

Col BLIMP

Gad, sir, Lord Beaverbrook is right. The Austrians celebrated Hitler's birthday just to show how thankful they were he wasn't twins.

BLIMP SAYS—

Gad, sir, Lord Ashcan is right. Hitler only needs arms so that he can declare peace on the rest of the world.

SPLASH BY BLIMP

Gad, sir, Ribbentrop is right. No Austrian "plebiscite" can be fair unless Hitler has won it beforehand.

Gad, sir, Lord Beaverbrook is right. It looks as though Hitler means to allow only Aryan Jews to make a living in Germany.

HIGH NOTE BY BLIMP

80

Gad, sir, Lord Guzzle is right. Those Germans in N.W. Africa demanding political freedom need a fellow like Hitler to deal with them.

COL. BLIMP—OVER !

Gad, sir, Lord Beaverbrook is right. All that Hitler has done is to cure the Austrians of being Austrians. A great patriot, sir.

COL BLIMP CRISIS

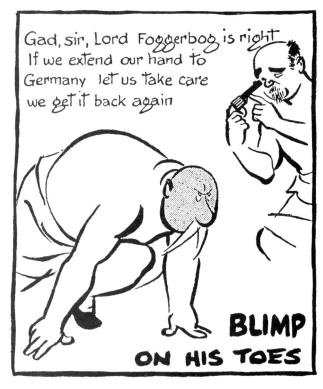

2. LOW AND BLIMP

'THE WORLD AND COLONEL BLIMP'

David Low (*Low's Political Parade*, 1936)

I REGRET that, contrary to the custom now established among authors, I am unable to declare that 'the characters in this book are entirely fictitious'. As one convinced sceptic of human greatness to another, I agree that Hitler, Mussolini, Roosevelt, Baldwin and MacDonald probably have no real existence; but I am perfectly sure that Colonel Blimp exists, obstinately and ubiquitously; though it is true that his elements rarely reach a concentrated form capable of manifestation as a personality except in the hot room of my Turkish bath.

When, amid the blasts of hell, the towel is torn aside, the secret places of the heart are revealed. Of Colonel Blimp it could never be said that his discretion was more than his eloquence, nor of me that my use of speech was to conceal my thoughts rather than to express them. We argue.

He has great faith in 'common-sense', which, naturally, he assumes to be the sense of his kind, exclusively; I, on the other hand, prefer my sense uncommon. We concur upon the fundamentals, being both in favour of Happiness and Prosperity; it is only in the details that we disagree. In general to me the views of Blimp are sentimental, that is to say variable and at times incompatible, and he inclines to the status quo anti-almost-everything; whereas I am realistic, and I do not feel called upon to cramp my ratiocinative style by assuming as an absolute condition precedent that the only way to mend the present is to put a patch on the past.

It is upon the subject of war and the apparent difficulty of separating the honour and prestige of nations from the manufacture of lethal noises and smells that Blimp reaches his greatest heights of eloquence. Far be it from me to represent him as a man of blood, though he is too ready, I think, to regard violence as a glorious alternative to argument, and to exhibit wars as the triumphs, rather than the failures of man. In the presence of Blimp it seems a vain hope that civilization will ever be able to dispense with force, for one is reminded that human beings are unequally sane, and that the best-ordered community imaginable could be imperilled by the presence of one free demented Blimp. When the Colonel puts the view that the sanctity of human life is much exaggerated, I incline to assent that it might be excusable to kill him.

The need for the defence of My Country is ever before Blimp. Let it not be imagined that 'My Country' carries any narrow proprietorial, or even territorial, implication; for it would be inadequate and unjust to picture Blimp defending to the death our Turkish bath merely, or limited to preventing with drawn sword enemies from diverting the course of the Thames. Neither take it that the people who inhabit the lands over which the flag of Blimp and me proudly floats are 'My Country'. The Colonel greatly admires, as we all do, an ideal British working-man whose most notable characteristics are Sturdy Independence coupled with Unquestioning Obedience; but in the world of reality the truth must be told that to Blimp the British working-man in bulk is an almost intolerable nuisance, with his everlasting grumbles about under-nourishment and his inconvenient yearnings for selfish improvement. Any display of Sturdy Independence in that quarter and Blimp calls the police.

Colonel Blimp will tell you that British-traditions-and-institutions are important elements in 'My Country', and this is so, if we push aside democracy and liberty and accept gold coaches, ceremonials involving large concourses of persons preferably armed and in coloured clothing, and high officials in strange hats reading things from parchments as representative British-traditions-and-institutions. More than anything else, however, 'My Country' is Britannia. Blimp would die for Britannia.

The devotion of Colonel Blimp to Britannia is to me only an illustration of the danger of cartooning. In the profession of cartooning it is expedient, even necessary sometimes, to improvise picturesque symbols to personify the impersonal. The method has its perils in a society of human beings with literal minds. Symbols have a way of obscuring reality and living long after the reason for their invention is dead; and there is nothing so dangerous as the living symbol of a dead idea. Thus, though quick transport, wireless and cinema have reduced the world's size so that the realization of the essential unity of the human family is obvious and commonplace, the symbols of division, convenient when the world was so wide that foreigners were mysterious, remain; and the commerce of nations is still, to Blimp, not concerned with peoples, but with a lot of gods called England, France, Germany, Russia and so on, playing a kind of Olympic games. Blimp, as he will tell you, is doubtful but not unreasonable about any League of Nations or whatever you like to call it. He will tolerate it provided it will not interfere with the Divine Rules of Cricket: each god to continue wearing his right cap and playing for his side, each being sporting to his opponent ('Sorry, sir! Hard lines, sir') and whoever wins, a return match next season. But naturally he has no use for any League that hisses his gods. All very well to want to abolish cricket, but hang it all, play the game. The only way to convince fellows obstinate on this point is to push them in the river and then point out that their arguments are wet.

'Do you believe in fairies?' implores Peter Pan when his litle Tinker Bell is

perishing of the indifference of mortals. 'YES!' shouts the audience enthusiastically, and Tinker Bell has a new lease of life.

'Do you believe in fairies?' pleads the Primitive Man. Up go the hands to the appropriate salute. The bodies stiffen at the appropriate tune. The world's Blimps burst forth into song: 'Deutschland deutschland über alles allons enfants de la patrie God save our gracious king giovanezza giovanezza primavera di belezza land of hope and glory kimigayo wa chiyo ni ya chiyo ni . . .'

I suspect that when Blimp goes to the cinema he has a strong reflex impulse to raise his hand when one of the fashionable dictators appears on the screen, resisting only because the fellow wears the opposition cap. For dictatorships — that is, dictatorships of the Right People — live on the gods and can therefore be depended upon more than others to keep them going.

It is not the least attractive feature of dictatorships that in arranging their picturesque bouts of heroic competition, they find it necessary to crack the heads of misguided advocates of co-operation such as socialists and communists. Blimp's fear of socialism and communism, which are to him the same thing, amounts almost to persecution-mania. Socialism is no system of economics to the sentimental Blimp. It is a plot. But then all social and political movements are plots to Blimp. Restlessness among the lower orders is always due to a plot hatched by a number of bearded persons ten thousand miles away. Behind every political change lies inevitably some company of hook-nosed crooks, of Free-Masons, of Catholics, of Jews or of What-not determined to reap advantage by fomenting trouble. I, on the contrary, am unconvinced about all this cleverness. To me there always seemed to be more stupidity than wickedness in the world. I do not believe in the necessity of plots. No plot would be required to make Colonel Blimp uneasy if he were deprived of his dinner.

In connection with socialists and communists, neither democracy nor liberty are to be accepted by Blimp as important British-traditions-and-institutions. But, for the matter of that, probably socialists and communists would not accept them in connection with Blimp either, without careful definition. Doctrinaires might, for instance, dispute the liberty of 'the Blimp classes' to stop them from getting food and shelter. If, in such an interesting argument, Blimp's characteristic obstinacy in preferring violence to reason precipitated a revolution in which liberty and democracy were threatened, I [. . .] would have to step in and insist on an economic rather than a political revolution; that is to say, of the kind that aims at a redistribution of economic power, not a redistribution of hokum. Whether Lenin was right or wrong it is a point in his favour that he did not find it necessary to put on uniform and be a hero.

In contrast to Blimp's dislike of change in economics, as in politics, is his warm response to the bedtime stories of the Established Church of Mammon. He has a child-like faith in the economic oracles who see the Return of Prosperity every time the Chancellor of one country picks the pocket of the Chancellor of another; and in wizards of Sound Finance who explain to the depressed masses that, at the present rate of progress, if nobody has any babies in the meantime, the unemployment problem should be in hand by AD 2000.

Blimp does not, fortunately, expect me to agree with his oracles; indeed they do not agree with themselves for two days running. But beyond interjecting 'if the present basic assumptions are to be maintained' and pointing emphatically to the wisps of steam that curl about us, in our discussions upon economics I am usually reduced to speechlessness before his declamation of the latest leading articles upon the marvellous figures showing the wonderful improvement in our exports of fiddle-sticks. Flapdoodle is Restored! Gold Stocks Rise!

The steam is significant. If ever I get an opportunity I shall tell Colonel Blimp about a fellow called Watt who saw steam coming out of a kettle and got the idea of using it to push down a piston. From Watt prophets with vision deduced the rise of industry, the commercial rivalries, the Great War, and the depression of 1931 — on, and inevitably, after an unhappy interval, by a process of trial and error as it were, [to] a planned federal Europe, followed by a planned world in which at last man is relieved of the eternal preoccupation with scrabbling for the elementary necessities of life, and is released to begin civilizing himself. The descendants of Blimp will see to it that the process will be of elimination by convulsion, for they will be fighting for their world — a world of stupidity, waste and senseless cruelty in which only is it possible for Blimps to preserve their importance. But they will be fighting a rearguard action and they will find their last ditch.

That will be, of course, long after Colonel Blimp and I are dead; but what of that? Sitting in the hot room of the hereafter, we shall probably read about the end of his world in letters of fire on asbestos newspapers. 'Gad, sir,' he will say, 'you were right.'

'BLIMP MARCHES ON'

David Low (*Low Again,* 1938)

IT is the custom for all prima-donnas to say at least twelve farewells before collapsing into obscurity, so due reserve should meet the statement that the reappearance here of Colonel Blimp and myself for a return season may be, perhaps, our last. It must be evident, however, that the world is becoming a less congenial place for caricaturists; not because of any lack of material — there is no lack — but because of the increasing eligibility of that material in its natural state. The professional lily-gilder is superfluous when the lilies burst forth already golden. When 'the blue-behinded ape skips upon the trees of Paradise' in reality, the humble satirist retires, knowing then that he has nothing to teach the gods.

The art of portrait caricature became superfluous with the perfecting of candid cameras able to catch the great in their unguarded moments.[...] Privately, also, caricaturists are at a disadvantage. As the Boswell of Colonel Blimp, I, for instance, find that crass overstatement which I have employed successfully in the past for effect in argument evokes no longer the shock of discord, but rather sounds like an agreeable contribution, in the right key, to the thought of the time. The subtlety of irony is lost, sarcasm defeats itself. It seems not at all jeering or derisive to talk of how Franco upheld Christianity in Spain by importing Mohammedans to wipe out the devout Basques; or of how Japan restores civilization in China by reopening the opium dens closed down by the dastardly Reds.[...]

I contemplate changing my Turkish Bath. Vindicated by the passing triumphs of Men of Action, the confidence of Colonel Blimp in his own judgement, even when it is self-contradictory, now becomes almost insupportable. The worst of it is that our lines of cleavage are not so sharply divided that all the Blimps are on the one side. A noted pacifist once confessed that if all the good men in the world could be set apart and opposed by all the wicked, he might be induced to approve of war. Since I fondly believe that what passes for wickedness in this world is more often stupidity, I am more tolerant. The segregation would be instructive, nevertheless. There would be, of course, the anti-Geneva Blimps, saviours of the British peoples by astutely manoeuvring them into a position in which they can be blackmailed at ease by any partnership of gangsters; and the Isolation Blimps, who, in a mere five years, by avoiding co-operation with great cleverness, have gone a long way towards isolating themselves from their Empire and their investments. But there are others. Standing on one's head cannot hide the family likeness. There are, for instance, the inverted Blimps (or Pmilbs) who simultaneously press for 'action' and oppose its consequences; the Pmilbs who think they can belong to the League of Nations and the Peace Pledge Union at the same time; and the Pmilbs who, as a protest against war, refuse to be told how to wear a gas mask. A confused batch of innocent treason for a totalitarian headsman — if indeed there be any satisfaction in beheading persons who are already, in a sense, beheaded.[...]

Although no intelligent man is taken in for one moment by the fakes of modern post-League diplomacy, it is still possible to persuade Blimp that Mussolini made war on Abyssinia because Haile Selassie had not behaved himself, that the Japanese are killing the Chinese for their own good, and that Hitler was preceded into Austria by 100,000 soldiers and numerous tanks simply because he was afraid of being kissed to death by welcoming Austrians. Blimp swallows the Hit-Muss postulation of Red Menace whole, despite its blatant pretence, with Soviet Redness so obviously on the defensive. It appears that it is the Reds that are the trouble everywhere. His hunt for Reds has become a witch-hunt surrounded by a superstition which is unconfused by a reminder that his own Neville Chamberlain, according to certain high-priests of anti-Redness, is a Red, and Disraeli, one of the greatest architects of his Empire, a dirty Red Jew; and unmoved by the fact that, in this country at least, the militant type of Red who habitually forecasts himself as Commissar is small in numbers compared to the ranks, who are so astonishingly trusting and disciplined that they would remain unmoved even if told officially from Moscow that Stalin had been arrested by the OGPU for being a Trotskyist and had confessed all.

With equal obtuseness, although no expert would deny now (after having made sure that shareholders were not listening) that the days of our old familiar competitive capitalist system are numbered, Blimp apparently believes the cure for everything is Confidence. Confidence in what? You may well ask. It was Blimp who recommended everyone in 1931 to All Pull Togeher, but omitted to say what to pull. The Colonel, I regret to observe, still lives in the old days when the British manufacturer was the Universal Provider in a world of little peasant customers. It penetrates his skull only dimly that the world has changed into a street of high-power self-supplying Woolworths, nobody wanting to buy, but everybody under an urgent necessity to sell in order to pay the rent. Although, as Blimp points out, we need have no fear about the supply of customers until the last Zulu has been served with a grand piano, I see by the papers that the economic wizards are about to start on the Zulus, and I fear the worst.[. . .] The idea of organizing the human race as a sporting event, to be run around and around in circles without any winning-post, is a profoundly impressive one to the myriad family of Blimp. Indeed, the idea of 'organization' or 'regimentation' is attractive for its own sake to their bossy natures, quite regardless of whether its object be constructive, obstructive, or destructive.

I do not suppose that the average man would object to having an organized morning if he could have a perfectly free afternoon; and I am sure that I do not object to organization myself.[. . .] But, after all, there is a difference between being organized for freedom and being organized for repression. The pride of the average man in his freedom is perhaps over-estimated (especially when slavery is called by a more genteel name) just as his capacity for humiliation is under-estimated. But to ask me to admit no vital conflict between.[. . .] democracy and dictatorship, is to ask too much.

'The struggle will not soon be resolved, though its outcome is inevitable,' says a non-committal statesman. 'And HOW!' I shall mutter as I smother Colonel Blimp with his own loin-cloth, and, locking the door of the hot room, steal softly away.

SPLENDID ISOLATION

Foreign Policy

BLIMP IN CYPRUS

BLIMP'S CHRISTMAS SPIRIT

Gad, sir, Lord Beaverbrook is right. The Government must absolutely refuse to wish foreigners a merry Christmas.

Gad, sir, Lord Beaverbrook is right. The Gov.t must sign no new pacts with Europe until we see how we get on at the Olympic Games.

STOP PRESS *FROM* **COL. BLIMP**

THE EMPIRE

Gad, sir, Mr. Eden is right. If the Argentine insists on printing our Falkland Islands on its stamps we must arm all our Post Offices at once.

IMPERIAL WELCOME

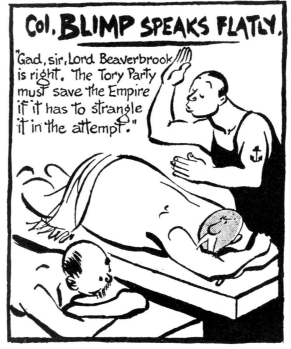

INDIA

Gad, sir, the Maharajah of Kapootle is right. There must be no monkeying with the liberty of Indians to do what they're dashed well told.

PUKKA SAHIB BLIMP

Gad, sir, Lord Bullswool is right. Do we rule India, or don't we? Then we should force the blasted Indians to accept self-government.

WHIRL ON THIN ICE WITH BLIMP

SIT-DOWN STRIKE IN INDIA.

103

DASHED REDS!

DIFFICULTIES OF A CARTOONIST IN WARTIME

BLESS YOU, MR STALIN, ENGLAND IS PROUD OF YOU.

BLOW YOU MR STALIN, ENGLAND IS SURPRISED AT YOU.

BLAST YOU, MR STALIN ENGLAND IS DISGUSTED AT YOU.

CARTOON CENSOR: Gad, sir, we can't pass this. It's friendly.

LOW: What about turning it sideways?
C.C.: No. Now we're getting the worst of it.

LOW: Well, t'other way up?
C.C.: Quaite, quaite. PASS!

DECONTAMINATION BLIMP

Gad, sir, Lord Cauliflower is right, At all cost we should have prevented Bolshevism from going Russian.

THE NEW MEMBER

BLIMP'S STRONG HAND AT THE HELM

Gad, sir, Lord Fishpatty is right. Before we allow Russia to protect the British Empire we must insist on her restoring the Capitalist System.

Forward, men!

the cads!

Gad, sir, shoot 'em all down!

HEAT WAVE IN REGENT STREET

TEMPERATURE RISES AT OPENING OF ANTI-COMMUNIST EXHIBITION

Blimpian hosts argue as to whether they go in by front door or entrance for exhibits.

3. WAS BLIMP RIGHT?

'WE ARE PRESENT AT THE END OF COLONEL BLIMP'

'MARGINAL COMMENT'
Harold Nicolson (*Spectator*, 6 March 1942)

I n the *Evening Standard* of last Friday I observed with pleasure a cartoon by Low depicting the death and burial of Colonal Blimp. I was glad to feel that this stale old man was at last to be laid to rest. But when I examined the cartoon more closely I noticed that, whereas Sir Stafford Cripps was conducting the funeral with stiff decency, Low himself (in the guise of a grave-digger) was evidently determined to exhume the Colonel so soon as Sir Stafford's back was turned. I should be sorry indeed if Colonel Blimp were to be with us throughout the remainder of the war. For although I should be the last to disparage attacks upon the inelastic mind, yet I do not feel that in a very dangerous war it is profitable constantly to suggest to amateurs that all professionals are fools. I do not blame Low for having invented Colonel Blimp. The cartoons which centred around that grotesque figure were amusing and useful for the first three hundred times. Nor do I question the cartoonist's habit of distorting proportions. It is the misfortune of all carica-tures that, in snatching at an eccentricity, they create a type. I am merely appealing to Low to permit this old bore to rest in peace. Colonel Blimp, if the truth be told, is a figment of Low's mind. I am prepared to believe that when he was a lad at the Boys' School, Christchurch, NZ, David Low really did imagine that Colonel Blimp existed in real life; I am prepared to believe that at Sydney, or in the boat which brought him from Australia to Fleet Street, he did in fact encounter an old gentleman whose moustaches and opinions suggested to him the elderly grotesque whom he has, year in and year out, rendered so distressingly familiar. I suppose that were I today to comb this island with the finest of combs I might find seven or even eight old gentlemen who really did exclaim 'By gad! Sir!' and who really did hold and

NEW REGULATION AT WAR OFFICE:

**OLD-SCHOOL-TIE FLIES
ABOVE UNION JACK**

to show a grateful
nation that the
heart of the High
Command beats
in the right place.

express the fantastic views which Low attributes to the late Colonel. Yet I should wager that out of my eight discoveries, six at least would prove on investigation to be, not colonels, but unsuccessful publicans, actors or insurance agents, who in the course of their self-indulgent but frustrated lives had never experienced either the benefits of education or that modesty which comes from ruling other men. Colonel Blimp is as much a freak as the man who tames spiders and whispers endearments to them in the dark. Yet by constant repetition Low has managed to convince many men, women and children that the Colonel is in fact representative, not merely of the unenlightened in life and politics, but of authority itself.

The defect of mockery as a form of criticism is that, although it may begin by assailing the ridiculous, it all too often ends by damaging standards which are not ridiculous in the least.[. . .] The ponderous fantasy of Colonel Blimp has swollen into a vast excuse for deriding authority and justifying disobedience; the 'old school tie' joke may, unless we are alert, spread into an excuse for disloyalty and defeatism. In war there can be no excuses.[. . .]

The root of all military efficiency is discipline and discipline, if rightly understood, is an organized pattern of confidence. The men who fought at Calais obeyed their orders since they were confident that their leaders would not demand this sacrifice of them unless it were worth while. They had no conception that by their courage they would save the army at Dunkirk; they were given strict orders, and they obeyed them to the death. Yet if that great baboon Colonel Blimp had been allowed to intrude between their own bitter emergency and their confidence in their commanders, then in truth resolution might have been shaken and courage sapped.

SPRING SONG By BLIMP

Gad, sir, Lord Punk is right. We can't have the British Empire saved from defeat by Soviet Russia. Dash it, it would lower our prestige with the enemy.

'THE ASSAULT UPON MORALE'

Lord Elton (from *Saint George or the Dragon*, 1942)

I T was only natural that when a brilliant popular cartoonist required a sort of ventriloquist's dummy to symbolize dull wits and old-fashioned obscurantism he should have selected a soldier, the now celebrated Colonel Blimp. This popular figure did not appear until the 'thirties, when a National Government was once again reviving ancient memories by sounding, if more than half apologetically, a muted note of patriotism. But his prototype had frequently figured in Low's work. Thus in a cartoon of December 1929, protesting against an apparent decline in the still-flourishing fashion of anti-war, and anti-patriotic fiction, and the consequent prospect that 'the professional patriots, romantic hero-worshippers . . . and incurable halfwits' may 'again raise their heads', the Colonel's twin, though not yet labelled Blimp, hobbles, gouty and ferocious, in the front rank of a motley party of generals, girl typists and ex-servicemen, displaying placards such as 'Our fellows were all pure — not like the rude enemy you read of', and headed by a braying ass hung with war medals.[. . .] And yet anyone who will take the trouble to look back over the opinions invented for the egregious Blimp by his distinguished creator, will be surprised to discover how often, even so, it is not Low but Blimp who was right.

Not long ago the apoplectic Colonel, arrayed in his simple panoply of Turkish bath-towel, could rouse derisive laughter among the intelligent with such characteristic aphorisms as 'Gad, sir, Winston is right, we must have more armaments' (May, 1934); 'Be prepared with plenty of armaments and then there will be peace' (May, 1935); 'We must have conscription if Liberty is to survive' (1935); 'Gad, sir, Mr Baldwin is right. To ensure peace we must have plenty of airplanes' (November, 1933) — an interesting commentary, this last, upon those apostles of peace who once jeered at Blimp and Mr Baldwin for wanting aeroplanes, and now jeer at them for not having wanted them enough. In the last resort Blimp, after all, represented (to quote Mr Arnold Lunn) 'what was left in England of that feudal and aristocratic tradition which we were glad enough to make use of in time of war'.

Today Blimp is in the Home Guard, and his sons in the Air Force, while of those who derided him most eloquently some are in the United States, and others (as Professor J.M. Keynes observed in the *New Statesman,* in October, 1939) 'who were the loudest in demanding that Nazi aggression should be resisted at all costs, when it comes to a showdown, scarce four weeks have passed before they remember that they are pacifists, and write defeatist letters to your columns, leaving the defence of freedom and of civilisation to Colonel Blimp and the old school tie, for whom three cheers'.

Professor Keynes was right to associate the farcical symbol of the army with the farcical symbol of the public school, for both, in a sense, are relics of that earlier, feudal tradition which chose its leaders not among writers and talkers, but among those who lead their men into battle.[. . .] The obloquy of Colonel Blimp accordingly has its roots in powerful and respectable historical forces. A psychologist, however, could probably distinguish a dozen or so of contributory factors in the cult of this particular scapegoat. The traditional unpopularity of the Army, except in time of war, an unpopularity which had even induced the Iron Duke to take steps to ensure that henceforth, save when duty made it unavoidable, his officers should not show themselves in uniform in public; hatred of German militarism; fear of another war; dreams of permanent, universal peace — all these must have played their part.

The fact remains that essentially Blimp was the eternal dug-out (or at least that highly choleric and obtuse individual in the almost legendary dimensions which had lately assumed in the pages of fiction; in real life it is possible to be acquainted with a pretty considerable number of colonels without being able to recall a single Blimp). He was a *revenant* from the last war. And by now the prejudices of the reaction against the last war, and the men who fought it, had sunk so deep into the collective mentality of the British intelligentsia, that they had passed out of the field of reason into that of the emotions, and the critical faculty of many writers who found themselves discussing events, ideas, or persons associated with the war was almost completely suspended.

(*New Statesman and Nation,* 23 March 1942)

COLONEL ELTON AND LORD BLIMP

Sir, — Raymond Mortimer writes in his review of *Saint George or the Dragon* by Lord Elton (*N.S. &N.* 7.3.42): 'Sometimes he makes a shrewd hit, as when he points out that Blimp was often right'. So could anyone make shrewd hits and show Blimp right if one chose to cut about the original text of Blimp's remarks, suppressing the essential asinine twist and misdirecting the jeer to suit oneself, as Lord Elton has done in three of the four quotations he prints (with wrong dates). Here are two comparisons:

Blimp as originally printed.	*Blimp as operated on by Elton.*
'Gad, sir, Winston is right. We must have more armaments, not only to uphold international law, but to protect ourselves from justice and right.'	'Gad, sir, Winston is right. We must have more armaments.'
'Gad, sir, Mr Baldwin is right. To ensure peace we must have plenty of airplanes. Otherwise how are we going to drop messages of goodwill on the enemy!'	'Gad, sir, Mr Baldwin is right. To ensure peace we must have plenty of airplanes'.

Lord Elton's one sound quotation, 'Gad, sir, we must have conscription if Liberty is to survive', is, I agree, right for today. But it was wrong, I think, when Blimp made it at the World Disarmament Conference.

Low

(*New Statesman and Nation,* 28 March, 1942)

COLONEL ELTON AND LORD BLIMP

Sir, — If Mr Low is right in thinking that my omission of 'the asinine twist' at the conclusion of two of Blimp's observations distorted their meaning, I apologize. But I must confess that the asinine twist seems to me in these, and other, instances, to make no difference to the fact that the gallant Colonel aroused amusement by talking sound common sense. When, to take another example, he observed: 'Gad, sir, Lord Castlebosh is right. We must not neglect chemical warfare. The future of civilization may depend on our making a worse smell than the enemy', the asinine twist, though it doubtless made us laugh in 1934, does not prevent the Blimpism from appearing in 1942 a stark statement of fact.

May I add that in my book *Saint George or the Dragon,* I was not endeavouring to show that Blimp's distinguished creator was wrong about foreign affairs — everybody who said anything about foreign affairs before September, 1939, was wrong somewhere. I was suggesting that Blimp himself was in more than one way the symptom of a tendency in his period which did not make for an efficient army, and also that, despite its *reductio ad absurdum* by a cartoonist of genius, the gallant Colonel's outlook was not so ridiculously antediluvian as it once appeared.

ELTON

Old Headington, Oxford.

'IN DEFENCE OF COLONEL BLIMP'

Arthur Bryant (*Illustrated London News*, 23 June 1951)

T HERE have been ugly and disquieting rumours of the betrayal of trusts by men in authority; there have been proved betrayals of secrets by Government employees in late years that have endangered, perhaps fatally, the lives of millions of Britons and, still worse, of the enduring ideals which our people, for all their faults and human mistakes, represent. These betrayals have occurred.[. . .] because those who rule us and those who create public opinion have increasingly chosen to assume that loyalty and patriotism were unnecessary virtues, indeed not virtues at all. They were merely symptoms, we have been told, of a ludicrous and reactionary stupidity. The public servants who still believed in and practised such virtues were contemptuously branded as Blimps. Yet Blimp, as we are now beginning to see, was a far better and wiser man than the unstable and brittle intellectuals who derided him, and a far more faithful and reliable servant to England. The comfort and security we enjoy rests, as it has always done, on the bones of dead Blimps: Blimps who lacked the cleverness to see that patriotism and loyalty were humbug but, fortunately for us, did not lack the fidelity and courage to die for us and their own outmoded faith. And whatever weakness there is in our national position in the world today — and there is much — lies largely in the fact that we have discarded, in favour of others less faithful, our most faithful servants and their outmoded virtues. The suburbs of Bath and Cheltenham and the fading streets of Kensington are full of them.

LETTERS TO THE EDITOR

Lord Alfred Douglas (*Evening Standard*, 15 March 1935)

Sir, — It is difficult to understand how you can on the one hand publish an eminently sane and sound leading article like that entitled 'Hysteria' and on the other hand continue to publish the idiotic and halfwitted cartoons which your Mr Low inflicts on your readers.

Why do you allow this absurd person to irritate your readers with his foolish gibes at your own declared opinions?

Your obedient servant,

ALFRED DOUGLAS

The Editor of the *Evening Standard* replies:
Tributes have been paid to Low's cartoons by persons of every shade of opinion. We think that the great majority of our readers agree with us that Low's art is unrivalled. The *Evening Standard* gives him a free hand.

INSPECTION OF THE CORRESPONDENCE COLUMN

(*Evening Standard,* 22 January 1943)

Sir, — Some years ago your cartoonist Low set up in your columns an 'Aunt Sally' and for years he has been pelting this grotesque figure 'Colonel Blimp' which, if he did but realize the truth, merely represents his own limited intelligence and inability to understand anything outside the range of his own strabismic point of view.

It would be quite a good idea, and an excellent piece of journalism, to let Colonel Blimp answer Low in the *Evening Standard,* provided that you, sir, were strictly honest about it. To do as you have done, namely, to put up Low himself in Blimp's name to reply to his own misrepresentations and absurdities, merely shows that you are so conscious of the weakness of Low's case that you dare not allow a fair discussion of that case in your columns. The best answer to Low's crude ineptitudes is contained in the volumes of his own collected cartoons which he publishes from time to time. One has only to glance through one or other of those volumes to see that Low has for years been almost invariably wrong in his judgments of current affairs and that he is indeed a man of quite exceptional stupidity and blindness.

Why don't you get a real representative of the type and class caricatured as Blimp to answer Low? All you require is an ordinary, decent, Christian, English gentleman of average brains and common sense. There must surely be someone answering to this description even in your own office.

Your obedient servant,

ALFRED DOUGLAS

'WAS COLONEL BLIMP RIGHT?'

David Low (*Evening Standard*, 14 October 1942)

W HEN I was a youngster in New Zealand, cruel small boys used to play a prank on their simpler kind by egging them on to shout repeatedly what was alleged to be the Siamese war-cry: 'Oh wah ta na Siam!' Say it quickly several times and you get the idea. I am reminded of this by hearing that the Central Conservative Office has collected a dossier about Colonel Blimp and myself and propose to cull from it, for party use at elections, material to prove that Blimp was Right and Low was wrong.

Like other cartoonists, I am quite used to being told by clever persons what my works mean. I do not take the arrogant stand that my own opinion alone is of value. I am prepared to admit that half the effect of a political cartoon is contributed by the fellow that looks at it. However appalled I may be at the revelation of what goes on in the head of a customer-collaborator, he is entitled to express himself on our joint performance.

During the eight years since I first introduced Colonel Blimp to public life, his character, habits and parts have been defined, denounced and defended by publicists, philosophers and politicians the world over. *The Times,* London, wrote: 'Blimp stands . . . for that inertia in British policy which drives the quick-witted to distraction, but serves the valuable purpose of gaining time for reflection'. The *New York Times* wrote: 'Colonel Blimp is the symbol of all that's dull and stupid in English life . . . ' 'Blimp is not a result of the iniquity of mankind but a symbol of tradition,' said a paper in Shanghai. 'The cost of Blimp is too high,' said a paper in Peru.

He has been debated in the House of Commons, and been buried twice from the Treasury Front Bench, first by Hore-Belisha and next by Cripps. He has been broadcast about. 'Blimps do not know enough and will not try to learn,' spake J.B. Priestley. 'To be a Colonel, after all, is not conclusive evidence that one's a blot,' sang A.P. Herbert. (Naturally, among people with constipated imaginations, I seem, through Blimp, to have conducted a vendetta against Colonels; but it is surprising to find Mr Herbert, whose imagination is certainly OK, hobnobbing in this company.)

Lord Elton goes further and solemnly deplores Blimp as a subversive 'attack upon the military virtues . . . loyalty, courage, endurance, discipline'. Harold Nicolson, improving on that, opines that he is 'a vast excuse for deriding authority and justifying disobedience'. To Arnold Lunn, though, he represents, more modestly, an assault on 'England's feudal and aristocratic tradition'.

As a tail-piece, Wyndham Lewis, on the other hand, writes him down as part of a Press Plot to foment international discord and mass-murder.

Views of what and who Blimp is, then, vary considerably. Up till recently they have fallen roughly into two categories: (a) that he is a destructive representation of something bad, and therefore to be approved; (b) that he is a destructive misrepresentation of something good, and therefore to be disapproved.

Time rolls on. A new category appears: (c) that he is a misrepresentation of something good, which was intended to be destructive, but backfired on the artist because the misrepresentation only proved its goodness. The support of this view by the Central Conservative Office makes it worthy of closer attention. When it is affirmed that Blimp was right and Low was wrong, I am tempted to argue the point on both public and personal grounds; for here, it seems to me, is the justification and enthronement of error; and here also is the impugning of my reputation for omniprescience, which is very dear to me.

Was Blimp Right? It is time for me to expose this humbug. Boy, bring me the records!

I now rise to make shattering revelations. I conceived and sustained Colonel Blimp as a symbol of stupidity. Not of colonels, nor of stupid colonels in particular. Not of Authority, nor especially of stupid Authority. Not exclusively of the Right Wing nor the Left. Stupidity has no frontiers, domestic or foreign, partly, professional or social.

The files show that Colonel Blimp has made 260 odd appearances, the subject-matter of his reflections dividing up as follows:

> Military virtues (and vices) ... 7
> Feudal-aristocratic tradition.. 3
> Home and Empire policy....69
> Foreign policy 139
> Miscellaneous 47

It seems that Blimp, though he sometimes contradicted himself, was no enthusiast for Democracy ('The only way to teach people self-respect is to treat 'em like the curs they are'). He was impatient of the common people and their complaints ('To give the unemployed enough to eat is to sap their sturdy British independence'). His remedy for social unrest was less education, so that people could not read about slumps.

He was an extreme isolationist, disliking foreigners (which included Jews, Irish, Scots, Welsh, and people from the Colonies and Dominions); a Man of Violence, approving war, per se. It was good for the physique ('Bayonets bring the best out of a man — and it stays out'); and for the spirit ('Wars are necessary — otherwise how can heroes defend their countries?'). He had no use for the League of Nations ('Too many foreigners'), nor for international efforts to prevent wars ('Shut up Geneva, so that people can make war in peace').

In particular he objected to any economic reorganization of world resources involving changes in the status quo ('Never shall we yield our colonies, even if we have to buy a geography and find out where the blooming things are').

He whooped for rearmament while a chance of constructing Peace remained to be sabotaged. The arms were not for defence of any ideal or 'way-of-life', but to protect the overseas investments of his friends. Blimp believed in the production of these arms by private enterprise strictly according to the rules of profit ('We must not stop our arms factories from supplying the enemy, or they might not supply us and then what sort of wars would we have?'). He was opposed to mechanization. He favoured cavalry, and if we had to have tanks, the tank corps should wear spurs.

When the Dictators menace came along, Blimp didn't recognize it. To him, China, Abyssinia, Spain and Czechoslovakia seemed to be just dirty smacks at the 'dashed Reds'. He excused the aggressors ('The Japanese are only killing the Chinese to save them from their enemies'), ('How can we expect Mussolini to behave decently if we object to his dropping gas-bombs?'), ('Hitler only needs arms so that he can declare peace on the rest of the world'); he objected to the use of economic means to cramp their style ('We can't declare a boycott of Japanese goods because then how could Japan pay innocent businessmen for the raw material to make their bombs'). He was all for appeasement ('There's only one way to stop these bullying aggressors — find out what they want us to do and then do it').

Even when it became obvious that the British would have to fight he obstructed collective resistance, especially with Russia ('Before we can allow Russia to protect the British Empire we must insist on her restoring the capitalist system').

I am supposed, by inference, to deny Blimp's dicta, to represent his opposition. (I am responsible for Blimp's side, too, of course. But let that pass). Very well. That makes me a sturdy democrat, considerate of the condition of the common people; for more education; for international co-operation; holding war, per se as bad; for the League of Nations and united efforts to build a sane international system; for economic reorganization of world resources to that end; for piping down national arms while hope of constructive peace remained; for nationalization of arms production, for mechanization and up-to-date equipment; for collective defence with other States against war-mongers; against the Dictators, when they came along; for cramping them early with an economic stranglehold; against appeasement, flatly; and, when Hitler showed his hand plainly, for collective resistance to the limit, especially with Russia. Well, that suits me.

I know the Central Conservative boys are in a difficult position. Conservatives did most of the governing during the shameful years during which Blimp enjoyed regular publicity, and their doings were therefore one of the main inspirations of Blimp's commentary. Looking to the political future, something must be done about the party pre-war record. They have the alternative either of admitting Blimp was wrong, which would at least imply an intention to shun his company in future, or of brassing it out and claiming that he, and they, were right.

I regret to hear of an inclination to the latter course. Blimp is a controversial figure, I know, so there would always be some who were for him. But I confess that I never expected — nor wanted — to see him adopted by a party. Fancy the meetings at the Albert Hall with twin banners draped across the organ: 'Blimp Was Right', and 'Three Cheers for the Atlantic Charter and the Five Freedoms'. Hark! as the organ booms forth the strains of the party hymn and 10,000 voices raise the dome: 'O wah ta na Siam'.

'WAS LOW RIGHT?'

Colonel Blimp (*Evening Standard*, 15 January 1943)

I AM well aware after some acquaintance with Low, that the ethics of modern journalism do not include a respect for privacy, even in the bath. I endure Low's offensive habit when reporting my views of depicting me naked on the shallow pretext that Democracy demands the whole truth.

I tolerate his showing me in such absurd shape that people might almost think I was a cartoon of his imagination instead of flesh-and-blood. But recently he wrote of me in your newspaper as though the purpose of my existence was solely to provide a contrast to his own omniscience. WAS COLONEL BLIMP RIGHT? asked Low; and, giving a list of what he calls my past 'stupidities', answered himself in the negative. Gad, sir, I demand the right to reply. WAS LOW RIGHT?

In so far as Low's cartoons have meaning, it is clear that for years he has been in favour of Foreign Affairs. In my opinion the cause of the present war can be summed up in two words — Foreign Affairs. Gad, sir, a country like Britain with interests all over the world should mind its own business and keep away from foreigners.

But Low was all for those League of Nations cranks. I considered their international measures to abolish war were a menace to world peace. Try to stop fighting and you're bound to make trouble. If you want peace, the only thing is to let everybody fight. Safety first. Events have proved me right.

Lord Elton very properly admonished Low for his neglect of the military virtues. One virtue, I assert, he is incapable of understanding. I refer to LOYALTY. Democracy, Decency, Liberty and Civilization are all very well, but Loyalty comes first. Duty to one's side. Gad, sir, even when the Government are going over the edge of an abyss the nation must march solidly behind them. Lacking this supreme virtue Low was nearly always wrong and unsportsmanlike in his criticism of pre-war Conservative Governments, especially when they were trying to avoid Foreign Affairs — Manchuria, Abyssinia, Munich and all that.

Hang it, after making an arrangement with an aggressor nation, we had to keep our word and let the victim down. It was the only decent thing to do.

Our policy was Safety First. That is to say, Neutrality and down with the dashed Reds. We had no quarrel with Hitler or Mussolini. They were obviously the sort of people to whom, if one offered one's hand, one would take dashed good care to get it back again. In short, cads. But in common fairness, you've got to admit they cleaned up the dashed Reds. And there's no doubt that Hitler did a lot for German Youth — physical training, open-air life and all that. Pity they all have to be killed.

Low was completely wrong about Munich, and about Russia. Wrong when he said that Chamberlain made one mistake in not making a military pact with Russia, and another in making a pact with Poland without Russia. He didn't understand the position. The dashed Red armies were no good. Bolshevism had sapped their fighting spirit. The grave danger of making an alliance with the dashed Reds was that it would have lowered our prestige with the enemy. (In mentioning the dashed Reds, of course, I distinguish them from the heroic Russian people now defending their Motherland.)

Munich was a great gesture of peace. And Realism. Gad, sir, it stood to reason that if Hitler was conceded Czecho-Slovakia's tank factories, the biggest in the world, he would be satisfied and abandon further ambitions. Anyway, we were not ready.

Who was responsible for that? Low tries to make out that because Conservatives ran the Government from 1931 onwards it was their fault. But he is quite wrong. It was the dashed Reds. Mr Baldwin had to conceal the true facts of the situation in order to beat the dashed Reds at the elections. Munich 'bought time' for us to place ourselves in readiness.

Well, asks Low, why by 1939 were we not in readiness? Simply because the politicians — and Low — had so discussed the weakness of our defences that it had sapped the confidence of the War Office, and arms production had been seriously discouraged by the agitation for Government interference in war industries. Gad, sir, somebody should be shot.

Now a word on the Home Front. According to Low, his pre-war policy was Happiness and Prosperity, while I, he says, opposed Liberty and was 'inconsiderate of the condition of the people'. This is a travesty of the facts. I am a staunch upholder of the sacred British Freedom of the Press, but we can't let the wrong kind of people say or write what they like, especially with education rampant among the lower classes. Economics and all that. It creates unrest.

Take slumps, for instance. We all know how slumps arise — lack of Confidence. The way to deal with Slumps is to be confident that there will be a restoration of confidence. But how could confidence be restored when people could read about the slump? Low failed to realize that you can't have it both ways. He was wrong. One saw the disastrous effects of unrest among the pre-war unemployed in their failure to appreciate that if the positions had been reversed the wealthy classes would have been quite well-behaved on the dole.

What the lower classes have never understood is that unrest is always created by the dashed Reds only for the purpose of preventing the upper classes from being fair of their own accord. Today it is evident that the wiser course in the pre-war years would have been to have given the unemployed less food and spent the money on keeping them fit.

What of the Future? Hang it, sir. We are at war! Yet some people — including Low — are always agitating about What We Are Fighting For. They pretend to be doing it for the troops, but in my opinion it's not likely to encourage the troops to know that people at home are thinking about what they are fighting for. Gad, sir, the troops are fighting for Civilization, not for sordid ideals.

I'm all for the Atlantic Charter, of course, except as regards the British Empire. Gad, sir, what we have we'll hold if we can get it back. We hear a lot nowadays about the Colonies from the dashed Reds. They always try to blacken the administration and whitewash the natives. Self-determination is all very well. Difficulty is that these natives don't understand Patriotism. Give 'em an inch and they want to run their own countries. After all, we are fighting this war to protect the rights of small peoples, so there must be no monkeying with the Liberty of the natives to do as they're dashed well told.

What about the Home Front? Low supports these dashed Nosey Parkers running about planning everything. Absolute anarchy. Fellows always wanting to improve the British way of life. Dashed unpatriotic. These Planners say they are out to avoid chaos. Say what you like about chaos, it provides complete freedom for Enterprise and Initiative. And what is going to be needed more after the war than Enterprise and Initiative?

First, you've got these dashed vista-mongers wanting to tell people what to do with their own land. With six million new houses to build we shall be too busy to plan what they will look like or where we will put 'em. 'The Land for the People', indeed? Well, aren't the Duke of Westminster and the Marquess of Bute people? Sheer class distinction.

Then there's the Bishops. 'Public Control of Credit, Land and Water!' Dash it, you can't mix religion with business. It's unethical. What this country needs is a religious revival against the teachings of the Archbishop of Canterbury. And now we have this fellow Beveridge wanting to undermine the stability of the country with Security.

The grave danger of Security is that it will sap the sturdy British independence of the working classes. Who's going to have Initiative and Enterprise if he has £2 per week! (I except, of course, those in the higher income brackets.) Everybody knows that insurance discourages thrift even more than saving does.

As for Beveridge's free doctoring proposal, all this compulsory public health will rot the stamina of the nation. They'll be making the doctors into a union next. It should be reported to the British Medical Association. Gad, sir, we are fighting for Freedom, but what with the Post Office, Income Tax, the London Passenger Transport, the Bishops and Beveridge, we might as well be under Hitler. Rank totalitarianism.

Burdened with a colossal national debt, with our invisible exports vanished, our overseas investments sunk and all our markets gone, trading conditions after the war are going to be practically impossible. This is no time for planning. We must stand by the traditions and practices that saw us safely up to the Slump. We must stick to Capitalism as Nature intended us to. No Government interference. We must revive exports by prohibiting imports, thereby inducing a spirit of Healthy Competition bringing stability to industry and recovering British supremacy in world trade. We could whoop up the home markets, too, by strict rationalization. Costs must be cheapened by reducing wages, thus increasing the purchasing power of the people and creating domestic demand.

True, post-war conditions may involve some Reorganization for Efficiency. But the best people to handle all that are the Federation of British Industries. It stands to reason private people know more about what is good for the country than members of Parliament, because private people are inspired by the Profit Motive, which is the spirit of service.

A lot of bosh is talked by the Reds about the Profit Motive, but you've got to have people making profits or you can't have business development (except in Russia, where they don't understand economics). The great danger of concentrating industrial power under public control is that any adventurer may get a majority of votes and then command the lot. Too dangerous. Much safer to hand the whole thing over to private monopolies that aren't dependent upon votes and can't be interfered with.

Later on, perhaps, the Government might send a commission to the FBI to try to secure their support for Democracy.

It appears certain now that victory will be won as soon as we have defeated the enemy. True Englishmen will never sheath the sword until Freedom is restored and until Low, the dashed Reds and the dashed planners are all locked up. Let us put our backs to the wall with stiff upper lips and all pull together against Government interference and the future will be before us.

FIGHTING TALK

The Warrior Blimp

SCOTS GREYS VICTORY

Those romantic turtles at the War Office appear to think that fancy dress and the obsolete horse are still a great incentive to recruiting.

"JOIN UP TO DAY, MEN! WE'LL SOON SHOW THAT FELLOW NAPOLEON WHO'S MASTER!"

Unrest has followed the news that the War Office is to retire compulsorily large numbers of senior officers.

A tattoo of Colonels in Hyde Park was addressed by Col. Blimp. A military coup is feared.

Col. BLIMP UNDER STEAM

Gad, sir, Yates-Brown is right. Wars are necessary — otherwise how can heroes defend their countries?

RUN BY BLIMP

SMASH
BY
COLONEL BLIMP

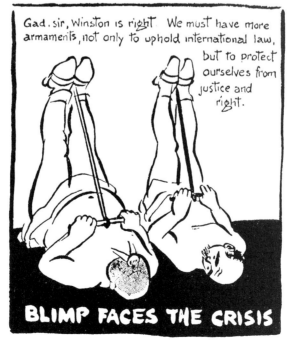

THE KEY.

134

COL BLIMP'S MESSAGE TO THE NATION.

THE TURKISH BATH.

Gad, sir, Lord Fevermere is right. We must not stop our arms factories from supplying the enemy, or they might become unable to supply us, and then what sort of wars would we have?

BLIMP PEACE BALLOT
SIGN TODAY

1 Q. Are you in favour of shutting up Geneva so that people may make war in peace?

A. Gad, sir, yes!

2 Q. Are you in favour of increasing armaments to defend Lord Bunk's investments?

A. Gad, sir, yes!

favour of conscription of wealth?

A. No. No! Certainly NOT, sir! No! No!

Sign here

Gad, we
should persist in our
present policy of victor-
ious evacuation, luring
the enemy to England &
giving him influenza.

PINSPRAY BY Col BLIMP.

Gad, sir, Lucy Houston is right. We need 5,000 more planes, otherwise how can the upper classes fly to Scotland when the bombing of London begins?

BLIMP BARRAGE FOR LOW'S HIDEOUT

As soon as the walrus moustaches grow long enough to entangle enemy airplanes, invitations will be sent to all the principal war-lords.

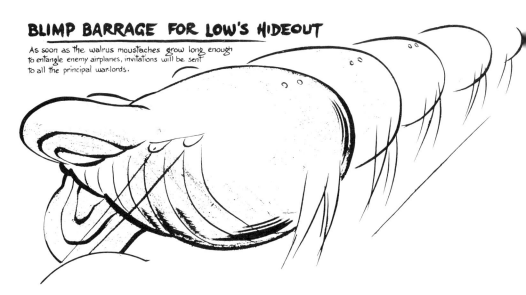

THEY SHALL NOT PASS!

PASSED BY CENSOR

POWERFUL CARTOON SHOWING
BRITANNIA AND BRITISH LION
PREVENTING ENEMY U-BOATS
FROM SNEAKING INTO THE
SERPENTINE.

Specially posed by Cartoon Censor Blimp and Musso, in person.

HANGOVER *by* COL. BLIMP

Gad, sir, Lord Sniff is right. The way to frighten these foreign bomb-dropping bullies is to threaten to take 'em up in some of our civilian airplanes.

BATTLE FOR BRITAIN—PART 2

LONDON SLEEPS

MORE ATTENTION TO THE OTHER END, PLEASE

THE WORST CAUSE IN THE WORLD
(WITH THE BEST PROPAGANDA)

THE BEST CAUSE IN THE WORLD
(WITH THE WORST PROPAGANDA)

ANOTHER TRADITION GONE

"GAD, SPREADING ALARM AND DEPRESSION, WHAT!"

COL. BLIMP ON GUARD

Gad, sir, Vansittart is right. Stalin has to keep Hitler going, because he can't risk a Bolshevik revolution in Germany. It might start a Bolshevik revolution in Russia.

Gad, sir, Count Vermacelli is right. It's simply dastardly the way the Russians go around damaging people's torpedoes with their ships

COOL-OFF WITH COL. BLIMP

CABINET MEETING DURING THE NEXT WAR.

COL. BLIMP LOOKS FORWARD

148

4. THE IMMORTAL COLONEL

'BLIMP ASCENDANT'

(*The Times*, 9 October 1939)

NOBODY seems to know who first called a Blimp a Blimp — that the name should have been invented independently by a small girl proves its felicity, for children are notoriously onomatopoeic — but it was Low, the cartoonist, who first gave to the Blimp a human personality and a military title.

Since then it is natural to think of the Blimp as a human being. With the sympathy of genius Low made his Colonel Blimp not only a figure of fun, the epitome of pudding-headed diehardness, but also a decent old boy, clean in his physical habits and friendly and sporting in athletic encounter. But it is only since he has taken to the skies that we know what a decent old boy Colonel Blimp really is.

Seen in quantity he suggests nothing so much as a group — or should it be herd? — of the kind lolling in a celestial club window. You can hear the 'Gad, sirs!' trembling on the air. All his movements are true to type. When he is on the ground, inflated, children are with difficulty restrained from patting him, and when he rises it is with a slow, good-humoured roll, with just a hint of short-winded protest at 'those fellers' on the ropes. Once aloft he takes the changing lights to perfection; gleaming silver, or softly flushed with rose or gold ('Port or Madeira, sir?'), now veiled in cloud, now telling darkly against the grey. He has brought a new beauty to the skies, and Constable would have delighted in him. Above all he brings reassurance, and there are few of us who will not confess to a slight chill when, for any reason, the skies are for the moment empty of him.

But the present concern is less with the physical appearance than with the moral values of Blimp. Never has any kind of human being come more appropriately and modestly into his own. He demonstrates what Blimps, with all their pudding-headedness, were made for. You do not look to him for observation. His function is to keep things up. Bloomsbury can easily get over Blimp intellectually, but it would take a clever man to get past or under him at his own intellectual level. Blimp stands, in fact, for that 'wait-a-bit' — in lowlier circles ''arf-a-mo' — inertia in British policy which drives the quick-witted to distraction but serves the valuable purpose of gaining time for reflection. Often by the time Blimp has finished ruminating — it is hardly thinking — the matter has settled itself. Nor is it necessary to assume in the construction of Blimp any of the ingenuities that have been rumoured. He does his work of keeping things up by his own bulk and by his attachment to the soil. This last gives him a full measure of that lumbering wisdom which resides in the basement of the mind — see Oliver Wendell Holmes. The top-loftiness, which Santayana has observed as the other constituent of the British mind, symbolized in the Royal Arms by the Unicorn, has to circle aimlessly over him. Let us then, while admiring the rolling movements and enchanting reflections of Blimp in his physical presence, remember also his moral values in the present emergency. Up with Blimp!

'DONT LET COLONEL BLIMP RUIN THE HOME GUARD'

George Orwell (*Evening Standard*, 8 January 1941)

THE driving force behind the Home Guard has been the common man's perception that British democracy is very far from being a sham. It came into being as an anti-Fascist force.

It is therefore the greatest pity that its actual organization has been less democratic than the spirit of its rank and file. The control of the Home Guard is almost entirely in the hands of its richer members, all too often retired colonels whose main military experience was gained before machine-guns were developed or tanks heard of.

Any position above the rank of platoon commander is practically a full-time job, and can therefore only be filled, unpaid, by someone with a private income. This inevitably brought the retired colonels into the limelight.

Perhaps in the last few months there has been just a little too much of the spirit of Colonel Blimp and the old-style sergeant-major — people who may have been useful in the days of single-shot rifles, but who are a positive danger in an irregular force designed for guerrilla fighting.

With the onset of winter and the failure of the invasion to materialize, more and more time has been devoted to parade-ground drill and more and more stress laid on heel-clicking and butt-slapping.

Precious evenings which could have been spent in learning to use rifles scientifically have been spent in sloping and ordering them. And the Give-'Em-the-Bayonet view of war, excellent enough as practised by regular troops in Albania or Egypt against Italians, has gained ground to some extent at the expense of notions better suited to volunteers acting on their own ground (for such are the Home Guard) which a few enlightened soldiers have tried so valiantly to disseminate at the Home Guard training schools at Hurlingham and Osterley Park.

The rank and file have not missed the significance of this, nor of the tendency to give all commands to the middle and upper classes.

It is not that they grumble — at any rate they don't do so more than Englishmen, in the Army or out of it, always grumble. But they know, especially the old soldiers among them, that a part-time force cannot emulate the regulars in parade-ground smartness, and ought not to try, since it needs all the time it can get for the more important arts of shooting, bomb-throwing, map-reading, distance-judging, taking cover and the building of tank-traps and fortifications.

These old soldiers do not question the necessity of discipline, nor even the value of drill. They know that a soldier's first job is to obey and that, on the whole, the regiments which are the best on the parade-ground are best in the field.

Even irregular troops suffer in morale unless they march in step, carry their bodies smartly and keep their equipment as well as their weapons clean. But that does not mean that a working-man with two or three medals on his chest wants to spend his evenings in dressing by the right or fixing bayonets by numbers.

In any army the spirit of Colonel Blimp and the spirit of Osterley Park must struggle together to some extent. The danger of letting Colonel Blimp have too much the better of it is that he may end by driving working-class volunteers away.

It would be from every point of view a disaster if the Home Guard lost its all-national, anti-Fascist character, and developed into a sort of Conservative Party militia, like a middle-aged version of a public-school OTC.

The working classes flocked into its ranks at the beginning, and still greatly predominate there. They saw in it the possibility of a democratic People's Army in which they could take a crack at the Nazis without being bawled at by the sergeant-major in the old-fashioned style.

And let there be no mistake about it, the Home Guard is much nearer to being that than to being the other thing. The men who are in it are proud to be there, they have done their job willingly and they are conscious of having learnt a lot.

But if they had the chance to speak there are three or four criticisms they would make:

They would like to spend more time in training for war and less in training to do guard duty.

They would like more — much more — ammunition and bombs to practise with.

They would like to be a little surer that promotion is on merit alone and has nothing to do with social rank.

They would like a whole-time, paid personnel for some of the key jobs.

And they would appreciate it if rather more of their officers were under 50.

'BLIMPOPHOBIA'

C.S. Lewis (*Time and Tide*, 9 September 1944)

It may well be that the future historian, asked to point to the most characteristic expression of the English temper in the period between the two wars, will reply without hesitation, 'Colonel Blimp'. No popular cartoonist can work in a vacuum. A nation must be in a certain state of mind before it can accept the kind of satire which Mr Low was then offering. And we all remember what that state of mine was. We remember also what it led to; it

BLIMP'S WAR FOR DEMOCRACY

led to Munich, and *via* Munich to Dunkirk. We must not blame Mr Low (or Mr Chamberlain or even Lord Baldwin) much more than we blame ourselves. All of us, with a very few exceptions, shared the guilt, and all, in some measure, have paid for it.

For this state of mind many causes might be given; but I want at present to draw attention to one particular cause which might be overlooked. The infection of a whole people with *Blimpophobia* would have been impossible but for one fact — the fact that seven out of every ten men who served in the last war, emerged from it hating the regular army much more than they hated the Germans. How mild and intermittent was our dislike of 'Jerry' compared with our settled detestation of the Brass Hat, the Adjutant, the Sergeant-Major, the regular Sister, and the hospital Matron! Now that I know more (both about hatred and about the Army) I look back with horror on my own state of mind at the moment when I was demobilized. I am afraid I regarded a Brass Hat and a Military Policeman as creatures quite outside the human family.

In this I was certainly very wrong. It may even be that the whole war machine of the last war was not in the least to blame for the impression it produced on those who went through it. My present purpose is not to settle a question of justice, but to draw attention to a danger. We know from the

153

experience of the last twenty years that a terrified and angry pacifism is one of the roads that lead to war. I am pointing out that hatred of those to whom war gives power over us in one of the roads to terrified and angry pacifism. *Ergo* — it is a plain syllogism — such hatred is big with a promise of war. A nation convulsed with *Blimpophobia* will refuse to take necessary precautions and will therefore encourage her enemies to attack her.

The danger of the present situation is that our Masters have now been multiplied. This time it is not only the Brass Hat and the Military Police; it is our Masters in Civil Defence, in the Home Guard, and so forth. Signs have already appeared, if not of bitter resentment against them, at any rate of an anxiety lest they should not abdicate, and that completely, at the first possible moment. And here comes the catch. Those who wish for whatever reason to keep their fellow-citizens regimented longer than is necessary will certainly say that they are doing so in the interests of security. But I say that the disappearance of all these Masters at an early date is just what security demands.

If they extend their power too long, or abuse it while it lasts, they will be more hated than any body of Englishmen have been hated by their compatriots since the time of Peterloo.

Mr Low — or some successor of Mr Low — will imprint their image indelibly on our minds. It will not, of course, be Colonel Blimp this time. Perhaps it will be Mr Mares-Neste. He will be, I think, a retired businessman who, having few brains, finds the time hanging heavy on his hands, and, being a bore, is the greatest nonentity in his neighbourhood. The cartoons almost draw themselves. We see Mr Mares-Neste rising, say, in the Home Guard. We see how endless and useless parades, which are an unspeakable nuisance to his more intelligent neighbours, are a pefect god-send to Mares-Neste: here is something to do, here is self-importance. We see him doing things which no officer in the real army would be allowed to do — parading the men without greatcoats in winter while he wears one himself, or practising ceremonial drill in wartime. We see him developing a disquieting tendency to theocracy and becoming fond of church parades, though he himself, perhaps, hardly knows his catechism.

An outrageously false picture, you say? I hope with all my heart that it is. But any prolongation of our Masters' authority beyond the necessary time, or any slightest abuse of it, will quickly bring this nation of freedom into a state of mind in which the picture will be accepted as true. And then the fat will be in our fire. All real and necessary measures for our security will be 'sicklied o'er' with the taint of Mares-Neste. The indignation which finally sweeps him away will, in its haste, reject any and every scheme of compulsory national service. If you want a man to refuse the nasty medicine that he really needs, there is no surer way than to ply him daily with medicines no less nasty which he perceives to be useless.

The future of civilization depends on the answer to the question, 'Can a democracy be persuaded to remain armed in peacetime?' If the answer to that question is No, then democracy will be destroyed in the end. But 'to remain armed' here means 'to remain effectively armed'. A strong navy, a strong air force, and a reasonable army are the essentials. If they cannot be had without conscription, then conscription must be endured. For the sake of our national existence we are ready to endure that loss of liberty. But we are not ready to endure it for anything less. A continued interference with our liberties which sets up, instead of a real army, some such ridiculous and (by itself) useless *simulacrum* as a permanent Home Guard offered by the Mares-Nestes — this, be sure, we will not tolerate. If we pay the price, we shall insist on getting the goods; if we do not get the goods, let no man dream that we shall go on paying the price. That is our present position. But the danger is that if you impose Mr Mares-Neste on us too long, you will make the very name of compulsion not only so hateful but so contemptible that our readiness to pay for real goods will disappear. Bad money drives out good. The Jack-in-Office discredits the fruitful authority. A permanent (or even prolonged) Home Guard will drive us into a frenzied anti-officialdom, and that frenzy into total disarmament, and that disarmament into the third war.

'THE MANHANDLING DEMOCRATIC TOUCH'

V.S. Pritchett (*New Yorker*, 13 April 1957)

I T is Mr Geoffrey Gorer's theory that in his heart every Englishman desires to be a policeman, self-disciplined, calm, responsible for doing his duty. His love for this ideal self leads to moral claustrophobia and strain, which the police force relieves by the homely unbuttoning device of policemen's concerts, and the nation by a profound pleasure in being made fun of by foreign, colonial, or American critics. These critics have often found this tolerance maddening. When Harold Nicolson, contemplating the cartoons of David Low, said that his Colonel Blimp was a 'vast excuse for deriding authority and justifying disobedience', he put his finger on the source of Low's success. The Irish forebears of this New Zealand cartoonist had told him the secret of the policeman's bursting buttons: the policeman longs for someone outside the force to give him relief.

The shrewd and mischievous Beaverbrook was delighted at the opportunity to annoy his Tory readers and increase the circulation of his *Evening Standard* by employing a cartoonist who crowned his career by getting Colonel Blimp down on paper and adding a phrase to the English language. Shaw once wrote him to say:

> Unhappy Low, lie down.
> Uneasy lies the head that wears a crown.

Not a bit of it — comfortably going his way during the most quarrelsome stretch of British history, Low has continued to preserve the normal and relaxed irreverence of the Commonwealth toward the English.

When Low arrived in London, the arts of caricature and cartoon had become refined and tame, England was in the doldrums of club culture. Fancy, well-mannered amusement, not satire and ridicule, was the aim. Humor was constrained by dignity, there was grace but not wit. Wit was private and kept to the cliques; satire was abhorred because it led to personalities and vulgarity.[. . .]

To a country that liked to think of its leaders as persons whose clothes fit their bodies and their offices, as mad but never without their dignity, Low brought the manhandling democratic touch. He made rank and office commonplace, turned politics into a galumphing merry-go-round. Colonel Blimp was divested altogether; this un-Roman figure was shown fat and naked in a Turkish bath. Low's enemies fell back upon the last resort of the schoolboy, the pun on names. Low, they said, in a flash of inspiration, was low. He was not merely vulgar; he was amiably vulgar, he was even cocky.[. . .] Low decided to stick to cockiness. At Lord Beaverbrook's, he called for strong tea at dinner. Why not? The Canadian tycoon had greeted him at the front door in his underpants. But the British did not go in for this man-to-man stuff; there is nothing democratic about them.

It was one of the club rules that you love your enemies. Only two politicians objected to being savaged by Low — the cruel-tongued Lord Birkenhead and the lachrymose Lord Rothermere.[. . .] Even if Low had wanted to do so — he lacks the morbid genius for hatred — he could not have quarrelled with these suave, iron-handed men. Where he did get into trouble was with his symbol, Colonel Blimp. Symbols are sacred; Blimp was a caste.

The Army, the Navy, the official classes never forgave Low for Blimp. This was pure left-wing treason; after all, the Colonel was virtually Britannia's husband. Blimp is a faded figure now. He belonged to the Cheltenham Twilight, to the age that might be called the Colonelcy. His apogee was the order for the Charge of the Light Brigade. Blimp degenerated into civilian life when Low took him over, and he became a rather mild creation, intended to mock a tendency in the thirties — the first clumsy experiments in Double-Think. ('Gad, sir, Mr Lansbury is right. The League of Nations should insist on peace — except, of course, in the case of war' or 'Gad, sir, Lord Bunk is right. The Govenment are going over the edge of an abyss and the nation must march solidly behind them.') But by the time of the Spanish Civil War, the division between Left and Right became deep and bitter. It broke the elaborate truce on which the class system was then based. Low had grown up in a society that accepted the radical assumptions; he did not have to go through an emotional experience in order to obtain his beliefs. In England, progress occurs through emotional experience and by dint of fighting and active rebellion in people who get pretty sour about their independence. To Low's admirers, Blimp plainly indicated a determination to have a left-wing government when the war was over, and the Blimp party knew it. Low saw to it that Blimp had the wrong views about India, Fascism, Hitler, and Mussolini; one of the rare attemps to hobble Low was made when Lord Halifax came near ordering him not to infuriate Hitler, but Low did not give in.

[. . .] The cartoonist's problem is to guess the receptivity of the public. Can the cartoonist make the public think for itself? And here is the danger; a great deal of the high-minded disapproval of unkindness or irreverence in satire springs from anger at being asked to think again. Far worse, we are angry with the satirist for threatening our contemporary sense of security. In a democracy, a cartoonist teaches people to think for themselves day by day only by doing a lot of daily arguing and listening himself. Low thinks slowly. He no more dashes off a lightning thought than he dashes off a lightning sketch. He has even had to invent himself. Like Alfred Hitchcock, he is given on occasion to appearing in his own pictures. That little face poking around the corner in his later cartoons is Low in the role of Everyman, surveying with astonishment the unsought acquintances in high places with whom he has been embroiled these past forty years.

BLIMP ON THE ECONOMY

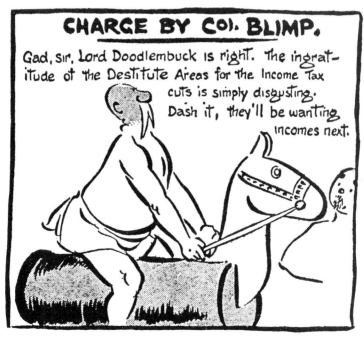

160

HAIL, THE NEW DISORDER

"DAMMIT, YOUNG MAN, WE MUSTN'T PUT THE CART BEFORE THE HORSE!"

YOGI BLIMP

Gad, sir, the Banks are right. The way to deal with Slumps is to be confident there will be a restoration of confidence in confidence-or something. What?

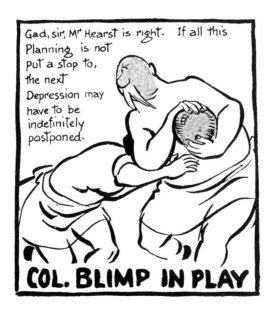

Gad, sir, Mr Hearst is right. If all this Planning is not put a stop to, the next Depression may have to be indefinitely postponed.

COL. BLIMP IN PLAY

DOUBLE HARNESS

THE HIGHER ECONOMICS

FREE MEALS FOR THE UNDERNOURISHED

"GAD, SIR, AT ANY RATE WE ARE RESTORING PROSPERITY."

"THE FELLER OUGHT TO BE ASHAMED! ENCOURAGING RAIN!"

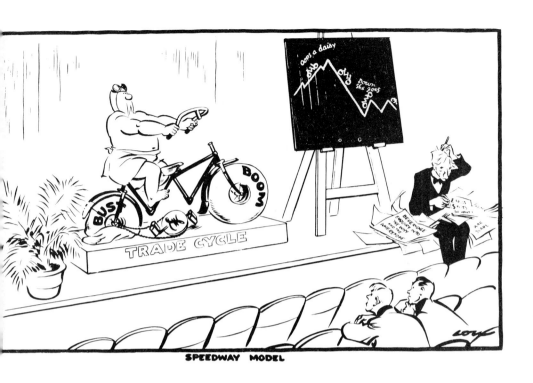

SPEEDWAY MODEL

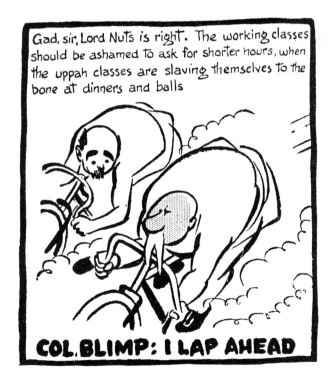

Gad, sir, Lord Nuts is right. The working classes should be ashamed to ask for shorter hours, when the uppah classes are slaving themselves to the bone at dinners and balls

COL. BLIMP: I LAP AHEAD

PATRIOTIC DUTY

"BUT IT HASN'T GOT ANY WHEELS, PA-PA!"

ENGINE? WHAT ENGINE?

BLIMP'S ALTERNATIVE TO PUBLIC CONTROLS

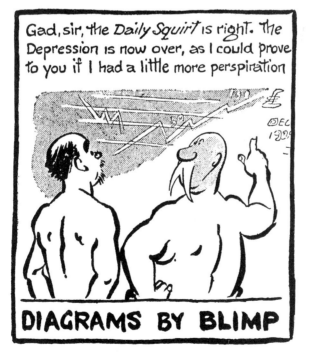

DIAGRAMS BY BLIMP

FAT HOPES FOR THE FUTURE

5. THE LIFE AND DEATH OF COLONEL BLIMP

WHITEHALL'S EVENING OUT

'THE COLONEL BLIMP FILM'

David Low (*Low's Autobiography*, 1956)

WHEN Michael Powell proposed to make a film epic about him, and Emeric Pressburger, his script-writer partner, spun his tale of *The Life and Death of Colonel Blimp* into my fascinated ear, I was too dazed with admiration of Emeric's phenomenal power of story-telling (he left Scheherazade standing) to find any reason for not agreeing. I woke up in time, however, to make two stipulations: that Blimp had to be proved a fool

173

in the end, and that they, Powell and Pressburger took all the responsibility. I enlarged my experience of life watching from a privileged position behind the camera the solid work of building up my simple symbol into a super-colossal two-and-a-half hour feature film. Amazing chaps, both blending social ideas with entertainment in their own medium for their own public. A different blend, a different medium and a different public from mine. I did not interfere. The product emerged at last as an extremely sentimental film about a glamorous old colonel whose romantic attachments nearly – but not quite – obscured the conclusion that if Britain followed his out-of-date ideas in modern war, we should all be blown to blazes. In the cinema, I am sentimental and I like films about romantic attachments, so at the première I sat in an obscure seat with a large cigar and enjoyed it.

Why not? I did not hate Blimp. I hated stupidity, but I would have had a bilious life of it had I hated all people that were stupid. Furthermore, my original conception of Blimp had been as a corrective of stupidity in general, not exclusively of that in hateful people, and it seemed to me useful to drop a hint that even nice people can be fools. This view, I was pained to find, was not shared by some of my erstwhile good friends and supporters, to whom the Blimp film was an outrage against their simple belief that, in political or social fantasy, hateful ideas must always be represented by hateful characters.

'Blimp de-Blimped', 'Attempt to whitewash Blimp', 'Blimp's answer to Low', 'Low's pot-bellied tyrant rehabilitated' were sample expressions of this view in the Press. 'O Low! O Low! What induced you to offer up your character . . . to be made unrecognizable under a thick coating of technicolor sugar, to be laughed at, loved and made piteous as just a dear sentimental doddering old fool?' wailed the *New Statesman and Nation*. Such innocence of the more subtle forms of persuasion seemed to me to be itself apt material for a few ripe Blimpisms.

Other eyes saw a different significance. Under the heading *Blimp Film Must NOT Go Abroad,* the *Daily Mail* waxed indignant at a 'gross travesty' of 'British officers as stupid, complacent, self-satisfied and ridiculous . . .' It appeared that the depiction of Blimp as a fine fellow, in keeping with the expectations of those who thought of him as a fine fellow, had had a double-edged merit in that, in their eyes, it imparted a greater verisimilitude to the whole, stupidity and all. 'We cannot afford', said the *Daily Mail,* 'to put out a burlesque figure like this screen version of Colonel Blimp to go round the world as a personification of the regular British officer.'

Churchill, the Prime Minister, was at the first night with Eden, his Privy Seal, and, I heard, formed some pretty definite ideas about it. According to my *Evening Standard* friends, he talked to his colleagues in the Cabinet and to Whitehall officials. Then almost every Government department sent delegations to view the film and give their impressions. Then six high-ups made the decision that it would not be advisable to let the film go out as representing the British Army.

Some months passed before everybody cooled down.

Nobody need have worried. The film got at last to the United States but on the way its Blimpish content had apparently communicated itself to its entrepreneurs. The poster publicity in New York showed Colonel Blimp (by an irrelevant association with a popular character regularly appearing on the cover of the magazine *Esquire*) as a lecherous old bounder leering at leggy females. That made me wince rather more than the unauthorized use in the Moscow Press by my old friend Boris Efimov, the Russian cartoonist, of Blimp as the personification of British delay in forming a second front in World War II. The latter was at least in character.

Blimp's life as a film star and a season on the stage in a revue sketch did not affect his life with me. For the rest of World War II he cropped up intermittently in *Evening Standard* war cartoons, in which, naturally, his connection with military affairs tended to elbow aside his other aspects. I could never be quite sure, when I entered a room where there were army officers, whether I was going to find friendly smiles or bloodshot glares. There were some awkward moments socially.

A memorable one occurred when my old friend Edward Thompson, the poet and novelist, arranged a meeting for me with Lord Wavell. The Field-Marshal was about to set out for India to become Viceroy. When I arrived at his flat I sensed a vague hostility in the atmosphere. I observed that I was not to be accorded the courtesy of privacy; another visitor was present, and I soon was frozen out of a conversation which became very technical on military matters. In time the talk switched to the irresponsibility of the Press in its comments on army matters and I found myself, to my surprise, faced by a Field-Marshal with a distinctly unfriendly eye, being bawled out about Colonel Blimp and his alleged part in this wrongdoing. I got sick of this. I seethed with repressed indignation. I said, icily: 'Sir, you are misinformed. Colonel Blimp is not a military, but a political symbol. Only about two per cent of his aphorisms are concerned with military affairs and those ridiculed your own critics. The only thing military about Colonel Blimp is his title.' There was an awkward silence. The other visitor wound up his business and went, leaving me looking for my hat. The Field-Marshal said: 'Aren't you going to draw me?' I said: 'Thank you, it is unnecessary. I will remember all I need about this afternoon', and left.

After such an unpromising opening one would hardly expect subsequent cordiality. But there was a happy ending to this story. Some weeks later I was pleasantly surprised to receive out of the blue a long and friendly letter from Wavell at Delhi about features of Indian life and affairs which he considered might interest me as an artist. Evidently the old man had thought again and concluded he had been unjust. I replied in kind. The correspondence left a fragrant memory.

When World War II ended there was just as much mental muddle in the world, perhaps even more than before; but Blimp as a character had become too identified with the pre-war and war years to fit easily into the post-war chapter. I could never have overtaken his military legend. Sometimes, when, twenty years after his invention, I come across his name in a newspaper spelt as an ordinary word without a capital letter and used as a synonym for military or administrative incompetence, I wonder how he might have turned out if in that Turkish bath of 1934 I had chosen to christen him Dr Blimp, or Bishop Blimp, using the same aphorisms, without the alteration of a single comma. Would I have been struck off the register by the British Medical Council for infamous professional conduct? . . . Would I have been excommunicated for subverting the Established Church?

Perhaps not. After all, it was a great and good Archbishop of Canterbury, William Temple, who said that it was not the ape or the tiger in man that he feared; it was the donkey.

CHURCHILL, BRACKEN AND BLIMP

P. Grigg (Secretary of State for War) to W.S.Churchill, 8 September 1942

I attach, as directed, a note on the Blimp film which is in course of being produced and which I think it of the utmost importance to get stopped.

The Life and Death of Colonel Blimp

The theme of the film is, according to the producer, the struggle of the junior officer in the Army against the obstructiveness of the Blimps at the top and his subsequent metamorphosis into a Blimp himself. The film begins with a collision between a young officer of today and Major-General Clive Candy, aged 66. The occasion is a Home Guard exercise for the defence of London. The young man starts his attack several hours before the exercise is due to begin and surprises the opposing general while the latter is still in his Turkish bath. This is supposed to be an example of ruthless initiative. The film then goes back to 1902 when the General himself was a subaltern with a similar intolerance of his elders and impetuous enough to embarrass the British Embassy in Germany by fighting a duel with a German officer. Then it traces his progress across the years in various parts of the British Empire, and so to the war of 1914-1918 and the post-war years. In the war of 1914-1918 Candy's playing the game according to the rules is contrasted with the greater realism of a South-African officer. Candy's attitude between the wars is a lack of comprehension as to why the Germans cannot realize that they were fairly and squarely beaten and there is no reason why they should not make and remain friends. A confused love interest (with three different women) also complicates the story at various intervals.

2. The producer claims that the film is intended as a tribute to the toughness and keeness of the new Army in Britain and shows how far they have progressed from the Blimpery of the pre-war Army. From this point of view he

urges that it would be valuable propaganda for the USA and the Dominions because in showing that we are conscious of any faults which we may possess, we are telling the rest of the world that the faults are being eliminated.

3. The War Office have refused to give their support to the film in any way on the ground that it would give the Blimp conception of the Army officer a new lease of life at a time when it is already dying from inanition. Whatever the film makes of the spirit of the young soldier of today, the fact remains that it focuses attention on an imaginary type of Army officer which has become an object of ridicule to the general public. In the opening scheme [sic] Candy is shown as Blimp himself complete with towel and everything. Whatever it may do elsewhere the film has made a character built up by twenty years of brilliant cartooning into a figure of fun, and there is the inescapable suggestion that such a man is a type or at any rate an example of those who have risen to high command in the Army in the period preceding this war.

4. There is the further objection that the Germans in the film are depicted as stiff and over-regimented in peace and as little more than very intense realists in war. The thug element in the make-up of the German soldier is ignored and indeed the suggestion is that if we were exactly like the Germans we should be better soldiers.

5. As stated above, the War Office have refused all facilities for the film, but production is still going on at Denham and the Minister of Information knows of no way in which it can be stopped. Steps have been taken, however, to bring home to the person financing the film the fact that it is viewed with disfavour by the War Office and that no Army facilities will be available. Whether anything will come of this indirect approach is at present uncertain.

W.S.C. to Brendan Bracken (Minister of Information), 10 September 1942

Pray propose to me the measures necessary to stop this foolish production before it gets any further. I am not prepared to allow propaganda detrimental to the morale of the Army, and I am sure the Cabinet will take all necessary action. Who are the people behind it?

B.B. to W.S.C., 15 September 1942

The Colonel Blimp Film

This film is being produced by Archer Films Ltd, a company entirely owned by Mr Michael Powell and Mr Emeric Pressburger. I understand that the production is financed by General Film Distributors Ltd, the head of which is Mr Joseph Rank.

The Ministry of Information has no power to suppress the film. We have been unsuccessful in discouraging it by the only means open to us: that is, by withholding Government facilities for its production.

I am advised that in order to stop it the Government would need to assume powers of a very far-reaching kind. These could hardly be less than powers to suppress all films, even those based on imaginary stories, on grounds not of their revealing information to the enemy but of their expressing harmful or misguided opinions. Moreover it would be illogical for the Government to insist on a degree of control over films which it does exercise over other means of expression, such as books or newspaper articles. Nothing less, therefore, than the imposition of a compulsory censorship of opinion upon all means of expression would meet the case, and I am certain that this could not be done without provoking infinite protest.

If you or the War Office were to let it be known to Mr Rank that it is your wish that the film should be dropped, I feel sure that it would be dropped. But I do not think that any approach of this kind should come from the Ministry of Information. As the Department responsible for Censorship, the Ministry is liable to be suspected of abusing its Censorship powers and requests from us frequently meet with a resistance which they would not encounter if made by a Department that has no connection with Censorship.

W.S.C. to B. B., 17 September 1942

We should act not on the grounds of 'expressing harmful or misguided opinions' but on the perfectly precise point of 'undermining the discipline of the Army'. You and the Secretary of State should bring the matter before the Cabinet on Monday when I have no doubt any special authority you may require will be given you. The Ministry of Information is the seat of Censorship, and consequently you are the channel for any Cabinet decision on the subject.

War Cabinet Minutes, 21 September 1942

The Secretary of State for War said that a film about 'Colonel Blimp' was being made. Facilities had been asked for from the War Office. These had been refused, on the ground that the film was likely to bring ridicule upon the Army. The producers had, nevertheless, proceeded with the making of the film, which was now at an advanced stage.

There was no existing Defence Regulation under which the film could be suppressed. He understood that the Minister of Information was averse from taking the very wide powers which would be necessary to stop this film.

More recently, however, an approach had been made to the financier who was backing the film, who had agreed that, when the film had reached the 'rough-cut stage' it should be seen by representatives of the War Office and the Ministry of Information; and if they took the view that the film was undesirable he would arrange for it to be withdrawn.

General agreement was expressed with the view that it was impossible to allow a film to be produced which was liable to undermine the discipline of the Army; and satisfaction was expressed that this could be achieved by the friendly arrangement outlined by the Secretary of State for War.

War Cabinet Minutes, 10 May 1943

The Secretary of State for War said that the film had now been seen by representatives of the War Office and the Ministry of Information, who took the view that it was unlikely to attract much attention or to have any undesirable consequences on the discipline of the Army. In the circumstances, he had reached the conclusion that the right plan was to allow the film to be shown.

The War Cabinet endorsed this view.

B. B. to W.S.C., 9 July 1943

Mr Arthur Rank, who is Chairman of Gaumont British, is asking if this Ministry can give him a definite decision about the export of the film 'Colonel Blimp'. So far we have been withholding the facilities for export by air which would normally be accorded to any British film of standing.

Is it still your wish that this film should not go abroad? We have no legal power to stop it, and indeed the statements appearing in the newspapers saying that it has been banned probably only serve to advertise it.

My advice is that the film should be allowed to go. At a time when the prestige of the British fighting man stands higher in the world than it has ever done, I think the circulation of this evident fantasy presents no dangers at all. But if you still feel strongly that it should not go abroad, I will try to find means of continuing our illegal ban.

W.S.C. to B.B., 11 July 1943

I think you should certainly stop it going abroad as long as you possibly can.

B. B. to W.S.C., 23 July 1943

You ask in your Minute No. M.459/3 that this Ministry should stop the film 'Colonel Blimp' from going abroad as long as we possibly could.

This we have so far managed to do by the unorthodox expedient of refusing the normal facilities for transport abroad by air. But even if we were able to persist in this expedient, we could not either by legal or illegal action prevent the film from going abroad by other means.

We have now had an official letter from Mr Rank, the producer of the film, informing us that he would show it in America and in the Empire. As the film is so boring I cannot believe it will do any harm abroad to anyone except the company which made it. And as this Ministry has no reason to protect the company from the consequences of its follies, I should propose to tell Mr Rank that he may make his own arrangements accordingly.

W.S.C. to B.B., 25 July 1943

I do not agree with this surrender. Will you please discuss the matter with me. If necessary we must take more powers.

B. B. to W.S.C., 5 August 1943

The word 'surrender' is not in our vocabulary! As a result of our illegal ban on this wretched film 'Colonel Blimp' has received a wonderful advertisement from the Government. It is now enjoying an extensive run in the suburbs and in all sorts of places there are notices — 'See the banned film!'

If we had left that dull film alone it would probably have proved an unprofitable undertaking, but by the time the Government have finished with it there is no knowing what profits it will have earned.

Air Ministry to Ministry of Information, 19 August 1943

We have had a further letter from Mr Rank requesting facilities for the export of the film 'Colonel Blimp'. He says it has broken all previous box-office records for the Odeon circuit of cinemas. In view of this it is becoming practically impossible to maintain our illegal ban. May we have directions?

MOI to War Cabinet Offices, 25 August 1943

Approval to release 'Blimp' has now been secured.

A BLATHER OF BLIMPS

BOOK CLUB WAR

A fierce battle is now taking place on the Reading front, the Blimp Book Club advancing strongly against the Left. Heavy casualties are reported including 29 unconscious and General Gollancz's spectacles blown up.

Gad, sir, Hore-Belisha is right. Nationalise the roads so that pedestrians can be killed under Government supervision.

COL. BLIMP'S REVIEW

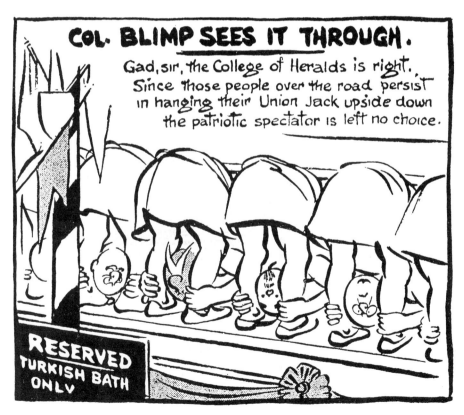

To the Editor —

Gad, sir, Lord Cecil is right. There should be a World Conference of Bathing Beauty Queens to agree upon a shape for the next five years.

Yours ffly,

Horatio Blimp
Col. rtd.

Gad, sir, Sir Albert Ashtin is right. Mr. Hore-Belisha must paint new lanes for motor-cars to cross the pavements in safety.

Colonel **BLIMP'S COLD SPRAY**

186

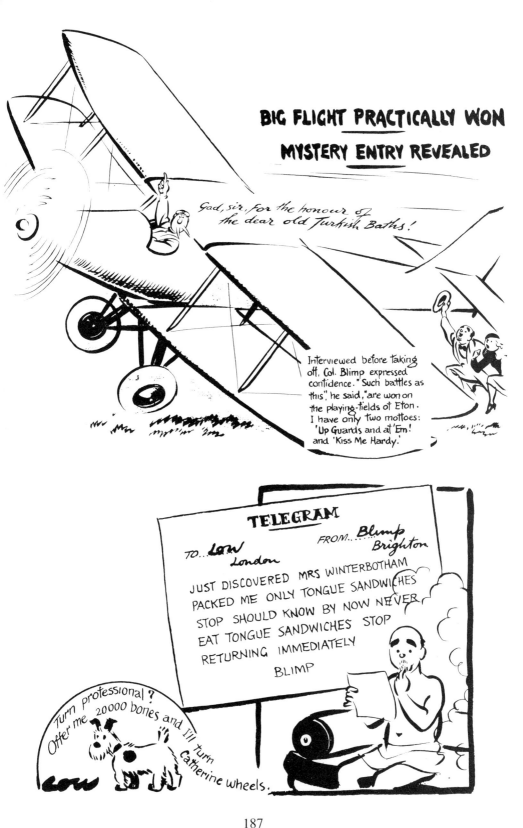

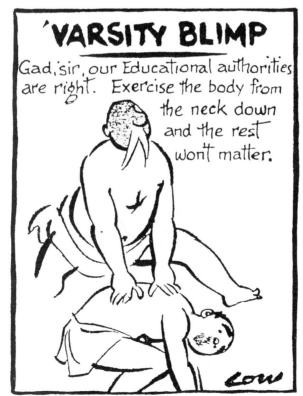

189

Acknowledgements

Grateful acknowledgement is made to the following for permission to reprint extracts in this book:

Nigel Nicolson and *The Spectator* (Harold Nicolson);
A.P. Watt Ltd, Crystal Hale and Jocelyn Herbert (A.P. Herbert);
A.P. Watt and the Trustees of The Robert Graves Trust (Robert Graves);
Illustrated London News (Sir Arthur Bryant);
The New Statesman and Society (Lord Elton/Low correspondence);
A.M. Heath Ltd and The Estate of the late Sonia Orwell (George Orwell).
'The Manhandling Democratic Touch' by V.S. Pritchett reprinted with the permission of the Peters, Fraser & Dunlop Group Ltd, originally published in the *New Yorker.*

Whilst all reasonable attempts have been made to contact the original copyright holders, the Publishers would be happy to hear from those they have been unable to trace, and due acknowledgement will be made in future editions.